"What do y[...]
I want, Lissa?"

She turned her head to look away as
he spoke. But as he moved even
closer she felt a peculiar melting
sensation deep inside herself.
"Don't touch me," she said shakily,
jerking away.

"I *am* going to touch you," Luc
whispered, staring at her. "You're
such an intoxicating mixture of
innocence and fire, Lissa. You blush
like a baby, but your eyes beckon. You
want me to touch you."

She shook her head fiercely. "No!"

"Liar," he breathed, smiling. "From the
minute I saw you on the beach that
first morning, I wanted to make love
to you."

"Is that why you told me all those lies
about Chris?" she asked angrily.

"They were the truth," said Luc. "And
so is this, Lissa…."

CHARLOTTE LAMB
is also the author of these

Harlequin Presents

and these

Harlequin Romances

Many of these titles are available at your local bookseller.

For a free catalogue listing all available Harlequin Romances
and Harlequin Presents, send your name and address to:

HARLEQUIN READER SERVICE,
M.P.O. Box 707, Niagara Falls, NY 14302
Canadian address: Stratford, Ontario N5A 6W2

CHARLOTTE LAMB

compulsion

Harlequin Books

TORONTO • LONDON • LOS ANGELES • AMSTERDAM
SYDNEY • HAMBURG • PARIS • STOCKHOLM • ATHENS • TOKYO

Harlequin Presents edition published April 1981
ISBN 0-373-10422-7

Original hardcover edition published in 1980
by Mills & Boon Limited

Copyright ©1980 by Charlotte Lamb. All rights reserved.
Philippine copyright 1980. Australian copyright 1980.
Except for use in any review, the reproduction or utilization of
this work in whole or in part in any form by any electronic,
mechanical or other means, now known or hereafter invented,
including xerography, photocopying and recording, or in any
information storage or retrieval system, is forbidden without
the permission of the publisher, Harlequin Enterprises Limited,
225 Duncan Mill Road, Don Mills, Ontario, Canada M3B 3K9.

All the characters in this book have no existence outside the
imagination of the author and have no relation whatsoever to
anyone bearing the same name or names. They are not even
distantly inspired by any individual known or unknown to the
author, and all the incidents are pure invention.

The Harlequin trademark, consisting of the word HARLEQUIN
and the portrayal of a Harlequin, is registered in the United
States Patent Office and in the Canada Trade Marks Office.

Printed in U.S.A.

CHAPTER ONE

THE first pearly haze of mist which always hung along the skyline was beginning to clear as the sun rose out of the sea far out on the horizon. A level line divided sea and sky at the furthermost limit of the eye. The air was cool and Lissa breathed it with closed eyes. Her favourite moment of the day. Soon it would be languorously hot and even the voices of the birds would sound drowsy, reluctant. At the moment they were calling melodically as they flashed past the palms flanking the beach, their gaudy plumage exploding like fireworks against the blue sky, busily searching for food before the heat became too oppressive.

St Lerie was a small island, one of those which had for centuries lain in French hands and whose outward culture bore strong French influence. Street signs, shops, had French names. The law was French in origin. Even the people's names were French, although few of them had ever been to France.

Lissa had lived there since she was four. It was the only home she could remember. Her memories of England were instilled by other people—myths, rather than memories. All her own past lay here, at St Lerie, and she loved the island for its beauty even if she feared it for the sudden, cruel violence which could erupt without warning, in howling wind or rain, or in an earth tremor which toppled buildings and took lives.

Luxuriant, hot, brilliant with tropical flowers in

impossible colours, the island was comparatively unchanged by the modern advent of tourism and Western ideas. Thick wedges of forest still covered it, choked with tangled dangling creepers, alive with snakes and mosquitos and insects. Most of the people lived along the coasts in small towns and villages.

Among the palms behind Lissa as she wandered along the beach lay the white walls of the Casino Palace Hotel, shadowed here and there by scarlet flambeau trees which grew close to the building. This had been her home for nine years. She had spent most of those years in a convent boarding school on the far side of the island, coming home for an occasional weekend or the long school holidays.

She worked there now, singing island songs, accompanying herself with a guitar. Lissa was under no illusions about her own voice. It was small and light, flute-like, a child's voice rather than that of a twenty-year-old. The guests seemed to like it, however. She had made her own translations of the songs, following the meaning rather than the actual words, and she enjoyed singing.

Ahead of her along the pale pink sands ran her dog, Fortuné, his short white legs racing as he galloped in and out of the surf which thundered up on to the beach.

'He crazy, that dog!' Gaspard often said, shaking his grizzled head in amusement, as Fortuné rushed into the sea to swim, barking, his white head bobbing up and down. Gaspard had been in charge of the gardens for years, his black face shining with perspiration as he methodically pruned or watered, singing the island songs in his deep, slow voice. Lissa had loved to follow him around, learning the old songs which had their own unique St Lerie flavour.

Glancing around, she saw a great wave rolling down on the dog's white head, which disappeared in the blue swell. Lissa stared in alarm, waiting for Fortuné to reappear. When he didn't she kicked off her sandals, unzipped her dress and dropped it on the sand. In bra and panties she ran down the beach into the water. Fear dragged at her heart.

She was so distressed that she did not hear the second splash which followed the launching of her own body into the sea, but she did hear the movements of another swimmer as someone drew level with her.

Surprised, she turned her head, the wet strands flicking across her cheek. A man's blue eyes met her own. She had never seen him before. He must be a visitor, perhaps a guest at the hotel. His black head moved alongside her for a second while he said coolly: 'I'll get him.'

'I think I saw him,' she gasped, pointing. She had just caught sight of a blur of white in the rolling blue water.

'Go back!' The black head shot ahead of her. Lissa kept swimming, despite his autocratic command. It was her dog and she was responsible for him.

He had an edge on her, his long body streaking through the water at a speed she could not match.

He dived into the rush of water, only his brown feet visible. As Lissa watched, sick with anxiety, he surfaced again with a limp white object. Lissa reached for her dog. The stranger gave her a wry look.

'Wait!' He struck out strongly for the shore again and she had no alternative but to try to keep up with him. It wasn't easy. Although she had been swimming since she could walk, this man was physically far stronger. The sun gleamed on his muscled brown arms and shoulders as his powerful strokes took him closer to land. The black hair was flattened all over his skull so that it looked like a sleek cap.

He waded up the beach and laid the dog down on the sand. Lissa tumbled out of the waves beside them, breathing heavily. The stranger was already kneeling beside Fortuné, his hands deftly moving, his strong body swinging in a pulsing rhythm as he tried to pump the water from the dog's lungs. She knelt beside him, biting her lip, watching anxiously.

'Will he be all right?' she whispered.

The stranger shot her a sardonic look. 'Well, don't ask me to give him the kiss of life!'

At that moment Fortuné came to life with an agonised yelp. He was promptly sick. The man released him and stood up, pulling Lissa with him, his hand coiled round her wet arm.

'Leave him,' he said. 'Even a dog needs privacy at these moments!'

Fortuné continued to be sick, shuddering, and Lissa exclaimed tenderly, 'Oh, poor Fortuné!'

'That will teach him to try to swallow half the ocean,' the stranger said with a smile.

Lissa looked at him gratefully. 'Thank you. You saved his life. I might not have got there in time.'

'You swim very strongly,' he congratulated her. 'You probably would have managed it.'

'I'm not as good as you are,' she said, shaking her head. He was undoubtedly one of the most powerful swimmers she had ever seen.

'You're built rather differently,' he murmured, his eye wandering down her, a faint smile curving his mouth.

Lissa felt her skin heating, as she suddenly became aware of her almost naked state. Her wet bra and panties were completely transparent in the rising sun. Thin nylon and lace, they clung to her slender curves and left her totally visible to the interested blue eyes observing her with such close attention.

He looked up and grinned, unashamed of his leisurely scrutiny. 'Charming,' he drawled, openly mocking.

Lissa looked away. Her dress lay some way off on the sand where she had dropped it. As she ran with a stammered word to get it, she felt the dark-haired man staring after her and burned with embarrassment.

She was very glad to snatch up the dress, step into it and zip it up. Slipping into her sandals, she turned, feeling safer.

Fortuné was on his feet again, shaking himself vigorously. She whistled and he galloped up to her, grinning widely, as though he had performed some magnificent feat.

'Bad dog!' she scolded.

He rolled an eye at her, licking her hand, and she lovingly tousled his wet head. His pink skin was visible beneath the short damp white hairs.

'He's pleased with himself, isn't he?' The stranger had slowly strolled over and was watching them, his long legs planted apart, his damp calves dusted with clinging sand.

Lissa knelt to hug her dog, shaking him, torn between relief and a faint lingering shock at what might have happened. 'You dare go swimming again at high tide!' she told him. He licked her nose and she laughed.

She felt a strange shiver run down her back as the dark shadow of the stranger fell across her.

She looked up, her eyes enormous, and met his eyes. His were a fierce dark blue which was made deeper by the golden bronze of his skin. He was the same colour from head to foot, indicating that he spent a lot of time in the sun, although not as much as a native of the island would do, since his colour was lighter than theirs. Some of the local men had skin like mahogany from hours in the sun and surf, their bodies constantly exposed to wind and drying heat. This man had smooth, polished skin which rippled like liquid gold over sinews and muscles suggesting a great fitness and physical strength.

'Are you staying at the hotel?' Lissa asked, shifting her startled eyes from the compelling shaft of his stare with a sense of odd uneasiness.

'Yes. I arrived last night. Are you?'

'I live here.'

'On the island? Or do you mean at the hotel itself?'

'At the hotel.' Lissa felt a deepening disturbance at the way he was watching her. She stood up, holding Fortuné's collar. 'Thank you so much for saving his life. I can't tell you how grateful I am.'

'Yes, you can,' he told her drily.

She looked at him in surprise, her eyes widening.

'You can have dinner with me.' He gave her a smile which lit up his whole face, the lines around eye and mouth cutting deeply into that golden skin, his blue eyes very bright.

'I'm sorry,' she stammered, her flush growing, 'but I work in the evenings.'

'Work at what?'

'Singing,' Lissa told him.

His dark brows flew upwards. He skimmed her again in obvious disbelief, the dark blue eyes narrowed. 'Singing?'

He sounded incredulous, and that wasn't surprising because at the moment, with her sand-stained dress clinging so closely to her wet body, her hair in saturated disarray, her small face innocent of make-up, she no doubt did not look like a professional singer. She probably looked more like a schoolgirl, she thought wryly.

She wasn't a professional singer, anyway. She only sang at the Palace because she was engaged to Chris. He liked her soft little voice and he had taken a chance on customers liking it, too. So far, luckily, they seemed to do so.

'I sing twice nightly in the cabaret,' she told the stranger.

'Really?' He was looking amused as he watched her. 'I must catch your act. Maybe we could have a drink together afterwards.'

Lissa looked away. Fortuné had wandered up the beach on his way back to the hotel. 'Maybe,' she said vaguely. 'Thank you. I must go now.'

He was obviously on the beach to swim. Looking across the sands she saw a rolled towel flung down, sunglasses and a book.

'Well, enjoy your morning,' she said, retreating.

He stood there, his powerful body gleaming in the sunlight, the brief black swimming trunks emphasising the muscled thighs and flat stomach, his hands on his hips as he watched Lissa walk hurriedly away.

She did not look round, but she could feel the blue eyes watching her all the way into the shade of the clustering palm trees.

She felt strangely relieved to be out of range of those hard, narrowed eyes. The stranger made her feel very nervous, very aware both of herself and him. It was a sensation new to her and one she did not particularly enjoy.

As she walked back up to the hotel she found him occupying her thoughts. Lissa rarely noticed their visitors; she was too accustomed to the comings and goings of tourists. The black-haired man did not fit into the usual categories and she found it impossible to dismiss him easily from her mind.

She left Fortuné sitting in the sun, scratching himself vigorously, and went into the back entrance of the hotel. Joseph looked up from the meat he was placing in a marinade. 'What happen to you?' he asked in his rolling Carib accent. 'You look like you been swimming in your dress.'

She told him and he roared with laughter, his liquid dark eyes dancing. 'Crazy dog!'

'He nearly drowned,' she said.

'That dog too lucky to drown,' Joseph said seriously. He was deeply superstitious, imbued with the island traditions. Although the staff were not allowed to gamble in the casino they gambled in private, often losing a week's wages on one hand. Chris said they still held cockfights back in the forest, out of sight of the

law, which forbade it, and large sums changed hands
on the outcome of a fight. Lissa looked at Joseph's
friendly, goodhumoured face and hoped he did not
attend the cockfights. The thought of them made her
feel sick.

She went to her own room in the staff quarters and
showered before changing into a skimpy white top and
brief shorts. When she looked at herself in the mirror
before she left the room she found a faint flush still
lingering in her tanned face. A slim girl of medium
height, she had very long, blonde sun-bleached hair
which she normally wore sleek and straight around her
face. Her skin was a uniform gold and her green eyes
slanted beneath the fine, thin brows she darkened arti-
ficially to give more depth to her eyes.

She was healthy, physically active and energetic, and
it was revealed in her figure; the rounded curves slim-
med with constant exercise and light meals.

As she thought of the dark stranger her frown
deepened. She had found his appraising gaze disturbing. Living at the hotel she was not unaccustomed to
being admired by visitors, but she couldn't remember any of them very clearly once they had gone.

Her years in the convent school had left her largely
very innocent and untouched. Her feeling for Chris
had obscured every other man from her. She had barely
noticed any of them, but something about the stranger
forced him on her consciousness.

He was unlike anyone she had ever seen before.
Most of their guests came partly for the sun and partly
for the gambling. They spent their days on the beach
and their evenings at the tables. Their attention was
not easily distracted from the ebb and flow of luck

around the gambling rooms. Lissa had learnt to recognise the various faces, the predictable expressions, of the hardened gambler. Their fixed excitement, their restless boredom away from the tables, betrayed them. She had felt none of that in the dark stranger.

He had had amused, self-aware eyes, a cynical sophistication in the lines of his face. Razor-edged profile, hard mouth, eyes which stripped and probed—Lissa was not impressed by him.

That he was handsome couldn't be denied. Men with shoulders as wide as that, bodies as superbly fit, were usually to be seen on the beach showing off their expertise in the water for the avid gaze of bored wives whose husbands spent all their time at the table. Looks like that, in Lissa's experience, often went with vanity and a slight stupidity. She had fended off grinning assaults from these beach lizards, before now, and been only too happy to leave them to the admiration of female guests looking for a holiday romance while their husbands gambled.

The stranger she had met that morning did not come into that category, though. She struggled to place him, unable to imagine him at a desk or doing some routine job. He had an air of such cool self-assurance, the look of a man who has no doubts about himself or life, yet who can laugh at both, take neither very seriously.

He was unusual. Lissa hated admitting it, but she couldn't get him out of her mind.

She went down to the offices which lay behind the hotel foyer. As she walked past Rebecca's office she heard the typewriter going. She opened Chris's door and the men inside the room stopped talking and looked round. Their faces had been hard and intent.

She caught a flash of something in the atmosphere which she had sometimes felt she saw before, but as always, it vanished before she had time to pin it down.

Chris grinned at her casually, ruffling back his fair hair with a lazy hand. 'Hi, sweetheart. Come in—we've just finished talking.'

The other men shifted their feet.

'I'll talk to you later,' Chris informed them, smiling.

They were smiling, too, as they filed past Lissa, greeting her one by one, while Chris leaned back in his chair, watching.

His father had been the owner of the Palace before it became a casino. Lissa's father had run the hotel for years and Chris had been as near to a big brother as Lissa had. Her mother had died when Lissa was six. Bitten by a snake in the garden, she had fainted before she could struggle to the house and by the time, a quarter of an hour later, she was found it had been too late to do anything to save her. Lissa's father had never recovered from the shock and he had never remarried. He drank far too much for years and it was a complaint of the liver that finally killed him while Lissa was still at school. Chris's father had generously taken over her education. When she left school it was only natural that she should come back to the Palace. It was her only home and, by then, Chris and his father were her only family. The many chains that bound her to Chris had been formed over a lifetime. She was fond of him as well as being in love with him. When his father, too, died of a heart attack, Chris had leaned heavily on her for comfort and support. He had been very attached to his father.

Lissa knew that she was both sister and lover to him.

He laughed at her anxiety over his gambling, but he tried to reassure her, too, and although he was too deeply entangled with it he nevertheless tried to keep it under control for her sake.

Chris was a man with a lazy, casual nature. He loved the sun and the sea. He had bright, laughing blue eyes and a skin as bronzed as her own. His thick untidy fair hair was bleached as fiercely as Lissa's. They made a striking pair when they were together. Chris had boyish good looks which lacked the sharp edge of the man she had met on the beach that morning. Lissa loved the easy-going charm of his smile.

'Fortuné almost drowned this morning,' she told him.

'What stopped him?' Chris asked, grinning. 'If he chews any more of my furniture I'll drown him myself!'

The telephone rang. He answered it and Lissa wandered to the window to stare out across the manicured green lawns. Sprinklers were fountaining across them, a rainbow flash of light in the cascade of water. In the flower beds which Gaspard kept so magnificently were hibiscus, bougainvillea, amaryllis and honeysuckle, the vivid gaudy colours of the fleshy petals too startling in the sunlight. Guests were beginning to stroll down to the beach. Some of the women carried the bright patterned paper parasols which the hotel sold—made by local women, they were very popular.

Chris had a whole fleet of women working for his shops. He sold a wide range of goods made very cheaply by local workers. Beach wear, from straw sandals to straw hats; gay metal or earthenware ornaments, jewellery, local paintings, hand-painted pottery.

'Pierre wants you to come down and rehearse,' he told her putting down the phone. 'That new song—he's done a new arrangement for the band.'

'Oh, good,' she said, smiling and blowing him a kiss before she left.

Although they had been officially engaged for almost a year, they had not yet become lovers. Chris had occasionally advanced a step or two, but Lissa's convent education and their shared childhood had made a sort of barrier between them which she had not yet allowed him to cross. Chris wasn't the man to force that barrier; he was too lazy. He waited, smiling a little wryly, and Lissa liked him for his patience. The decisions had all been hers. Chris would have married at once, but Lissa felt at nineteen that she was not yet old enough for marriage. On her twentieth birthday Chris had brought the subject up again and she had hesitated before asking him to wait a while longer. 'Give me time, darling,' she had pleaded, and he had grimaced and said broodily: 'That damned convent!' Lissa laughed, but she knew that he wasn't far wrong.

Girls who had been at school with her had tended to take one of two directions. Either they kicked over the traces violently on getting away from the convent atmosphere or they were shy and nervous with the men they met.

Lissa was not shy or nervous of Chris, but she was aware that her own attitude was bred by the careful disciplines of the sisters who had brought her up.

When Chris kissed her, she kissed him back lovingly but she felt no urge to hasten her marriage. She was half alarmed at the idea of it. It was such a vast step and she did not feel ready to take it yet.

That Chris was beginning to feel slightly impatient hadn't escaped her. When they kissed she could feel his excitement and was wary of it, knowing she felt none of the physical pressure she could sense in him. He never pushed things too far; he had never actually frightened her. Chris still felt protective of her, thought of her in the old brotherly terms from time to time. It was this warm relationship which made Lissa unsure of her own feelings and, necessarily, of his—she was not certain how adult their feelings for each other were.

She went down to the nightclub which took up a large part of the basement of the hotel. The lights were low and Pierre was picking out a tune on the piano as she walked in to meet him. Thin, curly-headed, he was a native of St Lerie himself. Gaspard, the gardener, was one of his uncles. Pierre had eight, scattered throughout the island. The family sprawled from one side to the other, involved in most of the local activities. Pierre was musically untrained, like Lissa, and quite brilliant. He had taught himself all he knew and could play most of the instruments in the band better than the current musicians playing them.

'Come on, girl,' he said in his soft island drawl. 'Listen here.'

She listened and nodded, liking it. The band were all local people, too, and had played together for months.

'Now, let's get real tight,' Pierre told her. 'Ready?'

They went over it again and again until she and the band were, in Pierre's favourite phrase, 'real tight', playing and singing the arrangement as close to perfection as Pierre would accept.

Lissa knew she owed her own musical education at the club to Pierre. He was tireless and merciless in his search for the best sound and he took no half-hearted work.

'You'll never be a world-stopper, but that shouldn't stop you working at it,' he told her.

He was faintly scathing about her little-girl voice. Pierre had a girl-friend with a magnificent, black-silk body and a voice that could break windows, but although on nights when Lissa was off, Chris allowed Jo-Jo to sing with the band, he thought their clients would prefer the innocent simplicities of Lissa's voice to Jo-Jo's shattering chords. Pierre did not agree—not just because he was living with Jo-Jo but because for his sort of music, Jo-Jo was superb.

He did not hide his opinion and Lissa secretly agreed with him. 'Gamblers don't want to listen to loud music,' Chris told him. 'They don't want to listen to anything. They want music that makes a low wallpaper while they think about the tables.'

Chris dropped in to listen to their final run through and smile approval. The song Pierre had arranged for the band was one of his uncle's favourites. It had a deceptive innocence. Under the limpidly sung words ran a visible strain of sensuality, an ambiguous edge to the words. Lissa had translated the song into English herself, but Pierre hadn't liked her translation; she suspected he thought it was too sweet. Pierre had worked on the words himself and Lissa found the secret echoes in them faintly disturbing. She was slightly flushed as she caught Chris's surprised and amused eye.

'Clever stuff,' he told Pierre. 'That's not how Lissa had it.'

Pierre shrugged his thin shoulders. His forehead gleamed with sweat. He had been working in the stuffy club for hours now.

'She hadn't caught the flavour,' he said, and Chris grinned.

'I bet!'

Lissa's skin glowed with heat and both young men looked at her with sly amusement.

'What're you going to wear, honey?' Pierre asked.

Blankly she said: 'I hadn't thought. Why?'

'Jo-Jo an' me seen a dress that would look fine with this song. Jo-Jo's aunty in Provence Square got it. Why don't you go down and try it on?'

'If Jo's Aunty Thérèse is selling it, it won't suit me,' Lissa said firmly. She knew the type of dresses Thérèse sold.

'Go on, darling,' Chris urged, 'try it on. It's time you started wearing smarter clothes.'

'Chris!' she protested, but was overruled. She found herself being driven down to Provence Square through the dusty crowded streets of the little town. Ville-Royale had been built originally around a shore fortress of which little remained now but the crumbling walls and some rusted cannon stuck fast in the stones which had supported them for several hundred years.

During race riots in the early nineteenth century the huddled wooden houses had burned to the ground and cannon fire had raked the crowded streets. Today there were garages, luxury shops and gay restaurants fronting the badly made road. Tourists in bright clothing strolled along in their straw sandals and hats. It had taken St Lerie longer to catch up with the twentieth century than other Caribbean islands, but they were just beginning to appear on the tourist map.

An unspoilt paradise set in jewelled seas, the brochures promised, and so far what tourists found matched that assurance, but as tourism made its usual inroads on the lazy life of the islanders no doubt things would change. Already prices in the tourist areas had risen steeply beyond that demanded in the unchanged villages in the island. There were more jobs but conversely more discontent.

The dress shop in Provence Square was housed in an old frame building which had been garishly painted. Thérèse was a large, slow-moving lady with a deep molasses voice and a wide smile. Lissa looked at the dress which Pierre had told Thérèse to set aside for her and her eyes rounded.

'I couldn't wear that!'

Chris eyed it interestedly. 'Whew!' he whistled through his teeth 'Try it on, darling.'

'No,' said Lissa.

Aunt Thérèse beamed at her and moved her bodily into the fitting rooms like a slow bulldozer shifting some light object out of its path. Lissa was still protesting with flushed cheeks and horrified eyes as Chris stared at her incredulously five minutes later.

'Wow!' he said simply.

'You like?' Thérèse asked with a broad smile.

'I definitely like,' Chris nodded. 'We'll take it.'

'It's expensive,' Thérèse warned without any real worry. Chris was looking at Lissa in a way that made it obvious such concerns as cost wouldn't even cross his mind.

'I couldn't wear it on stage!' Lissa protested.

'Wrap it up,' Chris told Aunt Thérèse.

'Chris!' Lissa burst out.

He grinned and his eyes glittered with excitement. 'Baby, I love it, and you're wearing it tonight.'

'I feel half naked in it!' The way Chris was staring at her made her feel disturbed. He had never looked at her like that before and she did not like it.

It was the sort of dress which she would have guessed Jo-Jo would choose—a lustrous black satin cut on the simplest, most revealing lines. Sleeveless, backless and close to frontless as well, it clung smoothly to the small, high breasts and fitted her slender hips like a second skin. Her tanned flesh glowed golden in the harsh electric light, the warmth of her body emphasised by the daring dress.

'Where did you get that figure from?' Chris asked, enjoying the unobscured view of it he was getting. 'Even in a bikini you've never looked like this.'

'It's this dress!' she wailed.

'I'll say,' Chris agreed, and Aunt Thérèse gurgled with enjoyment.

She saw them off the premises, beaming. Everyone on the island knew Chris and treated him with deferential respect. As they walked through the town everyone they met greeted Chris with a quick smile and a very eager word.

That evening Chris stood with her back stage, eyeing her curved body in the black dress. 'Baby, when are we getting married? My patience is wearing thin.' He kissed her, his hands lightly sliding from her waist to her slim, smooth hips.

'Liss,' he whispered huskily. 'Liss, marry me soon. Just looking at you tonight is driving me insane.'

She drew back, alarmed, from the heated look in his eyes. Chris met her nervous glance and grimaced.

'God, that damned convent! Liss, grow up, baby. I love you and you love me. What are we waiting for?'

Lissa did not know. She looked at him apprehensively, anxiously. 'We'll talk about it, shall we?'

'What else do we ever do?' he asked, his mouth wry. 'I'm sick to death of talking, Liss. I want to do something.' He did not need to expand on that, the urgent gleam of his eyes spoke for him, and her colour deepened.

She was relieved when she heard the band move into the final number before her own. 'I must go, Chris,' she said quickly, and he sighed, shrugging.

'Okay, but we'll talk later,' he threatened, half smiling, half grimacing.

She hurried away, so disturbed by the little exchange that she forgot the revealing nature of her new dress, her anxiety and shy embarrassment. When the crash of chords announced her she walked out with the blue spotlight shimmering round her, still dwelling on what Chris had said, and was quite taken aback by the whistles and clapping which broke out. Her green eyes opened wide. She looked at Pierre, who grinned, white teeth flashing, and made a circle in the air with finger and thumb, a triumphant teasing little gesture which eased the moment for her slightly.

She leaned on the piano, looking at him as he went into the number. Turning her head, the long blonde hair flicking over her shoulder, she began to sing, as they had rehearsed all day. The room was unusually quiet. Lissa was used to a constant low murmur as people talked and drank, but tonight they were oddly intent. She felt them quicken into amusement as the song went on with the teasing ambiguity which Pierre had given it. Laughter was soft, appreciative, as though they did not want to miss any following words.

Applause burst out as she stopped singing. She smiled and bowed, surprised and pleased, and as her eyes moved round the tables she saw a familiar face at one of them.

He was leaning his head on his cupped hands, his elbows on the table, his black head half in shadow. The light fell harshly on his lower face, throwing into relief the stark angles of cheekbone and jaw, the hard sensual mouth. The blue eyes were veiled by lowered lids through which she felt him watching her, but she could not glimpse anything of the expression in those eyes. Even so she was strangely jarred by something in the way he stared.

She sang one of her own translations next. It was a light, cheerful song which had originated on the plantations in the nineteenth century, a song the slaves had sung as they cut the cane. The grumbling impudence was tinged with the humour which she loved in the islanders. They had laughed, as they laughed now, at cruelty, tyranny, their oppressed condition, finding the joke even in slavery. It was a tune which made people's fingers click and their feet start to tap. By the third chorus some of the audience were joining in mutedly and she encouraged them with a quick smile and nod.

She went off to applause and the limbo dancers ran on to the stage. Several of them were related to Pierre and winked at her as they passed.

'Fantastic,' said Chris, putting an arm round her waist. 'Hey, did you see what was at the side table at the front?'

Lissa stiffened and looked at him in startled enquiry. 'Who?' She felt a strange anxiety as she asked that. Who was the man whose blue eyes made her feel like running away whenever they touched her?

'Lucifer,' said Chris, and laughed. 'In person.'

Dazedly Lissa frowned. 'What?'

'You must have heard of him,' Chris urged. 'He arrived yesterday. He's got a damned great yacht parked in the roads.' He looked wry. 'I hope he isn't going to milk us dry, baby. Why do you think they call him Lucifer? He's got the devil's own luck, and I don't fancy being bankrupted overnight.'

'Who is he?' Lissa asked slowly.

'Luc Ferrier,' said Chris. 'Come on, darling—Ferrier. Surely the name rings a bell?'

She shook her head, her eyes blank.

'He's always in the papers. He's the sort of gambler who never refuses the odds. A real wild one.'

'A gambler,' said Lissa, her voice filled with distaste.

'One of the biggest,' Chris said.

'A professional?' Lissa hated professional gamblers. They turned up all the time, people who lived by gambling, who drifted from casino to casino. Hard, obsessed and faintly inhuman, they seemed unaware of anything but the win and loss of the tables.

Chris shrugged. 'God knows. He may have a private source of money or he may live on what he wins, but he certainly turns up at most places sooner or later. And he rarely loses, and never for long. He has a lucky streak a mile wide.' He grinned at her. 'As I said, hence the nickname. I gather someone looked at his scrawl on a cheque and said: "So that's who you are ... Lucifer." His name looks like that, written fast, I suppose.'

'Don't play with him,' said Lissa on a peculiar strained note. She could not have said why the idea of

Chris playing against that man should bother her so much, but all her instincts cried out against the idea.

Chris was grinning absently, as if he hadn't even heard her. She saw his fingers stretching and clicking and her blood ran cold. She knew that unconscious little gesture of his—it meant that Chris was itching to play against someone. People who run a gambling house should never gamble themselves—it is too dangerous. Chris had an obsessive streak, a competitive urge to prove himself against other gamblers, as though it were a duel between them, a duel he needed to win.

'Chris,' she said anxiously, clutching his arm.

He looked down at her, bright-eyed and excited. 'Darling?'

'Are you listening?'

'Of course I am,' he said in abstracted tones, then looked at her with brighter interest. 'And I'm looking, darling. Liss, in that dress you do something drastic to my blood pressure. If you don't hurry up and marry me I'm not even going to wait for the banns to be put up. You've kept me waiting long enough.'

Lissa gripped his arm, taking a deep breath. 'Promise not to gamble against Luc Ferrier and I'll marry you next month.'

She saw the abrupt flicker in his face, the taken-aback frown. 'What?' He was evading the issue, hedging, his blue eyes shifting from her.

'Promise,' she pleaded, looking at him beggingly.

'Darling, I can take Ferrier,' said Chris, grinning. 'Don't get uptight about him. You're a funny little bunny, aren't you?' He kissed her nose and hurriedly said something about having to check on the front. She stared after his disappearing back in disturbed intensity. Chris had deliberately refused to promise not to gamble with that man even with her promise to marry him dangled as bait. Lissa did not like that. She stood there, biting her lower lip, and worrying.

CHAPTER TWO

SHE did not see Chris again that evening. As she walked through the hotel on her way to bed she ran into one of the croupiers, Max, a copper-skinned native with a French father and St Lerie mother, who gave her a quick, appreciative stare. 'Caught your act, Liss,' he said, smiling. 'Knocked them for six, didn't it? You're coming on.'

Flushing she thanked him, then asked: 'Seen Chris?'

'In the rooms,' said Max, half in flight, turned towards her with a grin. He was a handsome young man with a slim, lithe figure which looked good in the formal white evening clothes he was wearing. All the croupiers dressed well; it was one of the house rules. They wore red carnations in their buttonholes and spoke in soft, polite voices, but they were all as tough as Hades, Chris told her once. Born and brought up in the back streets of Ville-Royale, fighting from the moment he could walk, Max had a hard glint under his smooth manner. Any trouble which occurred at the Casino was quietly, discreetly taken care of by one of Chris's young men.

Lissa had never received anything but courtesy and a smile from Max, but she found him slightly alarming. She had the feeling he might well have a knife up his sleeve.

'Is he playing?' she asked nervously now, and Max gave her a quick, shrewd look.

'If you want to know go and look,' he said. He knew Lissa rarely ventured past the door, which was always guarded by several smiling men in elegant suits beneath which one could clearly glimpse the muscles of professional fighters.

Chris preferred her to stay out of the club, partly because he did not like her to get involved in that part of the hotel and partly because what she did not see of his activities there she could not complain about.

Now she bit her lip, shaking her head, and Max looked amused as he went away.

Everyone at the hotel treated Lissa as carefully as if she were made of icing sugar and might melt in the rain. The attitude had grown up during her childhood there. Chris's father had been very fond of her and had made her a special pet. Everyone else had followed suit, from Gaspard, the gardener, to old white-haired Uncle Joey whose only task for years had been to hang around the foyer and keep the uniformed bellboys in order.

If she had had a different nature she might have been spoilt by all the loving attention she had received, but she was far too serious and far too gentle. She had recognised the care with which she was surrounded and responded with loving affection to it. Even the tough boys from the dark alleys in the shanty town which tourists rarely saw had always treated Lissa like a princess. Their attitude, combined with her convent training and her own natural modesty, had kept her safely in a crystal case for years.

She went on to her own room, frowning. Was Chris gambling? And most important of all—who was he gambling with? Please, please, don't let it be Luc Ferrier, she thought desperately.

She took some time to get to sleep that night. Usually she fell asleep the moment the light was out and her head on the pillow. Health and constant activity gave her no time to dwell on the day's problems. Sleep normally just swallowed her up and what dreams she had were never remembered next day.

Tonight she lay awake, listening to the night sounds beyond her window, familiar and pleasant sounds to her but tonight oddly menacing.

Chris was a reckless gambler. Although his nature was lazy and charming, he became different inside the gambling rooms. When she had occasionally set foot in there she had found it hard to recognise Chris if he was playing poker. He was a man possessed, his handsome face excited.

She sensed he had no chance against the man with hard blue eyes and a cool aware smile. She knew faces. She had watched them come and go; bearing their nature in their faces. Luc Ferrier was outside the ordinary run of gamblers who came here. She had never seen anyone like him before. He frightened her. She did not like to think of Chris playing poker with him.

When she did fall asleep her dreams were filled with an insubstantial menace. She woke up several times, trembling, but could not recall what had been troubling her.

Next morning the air had that deceptive coolness which it only kept for an hour or so before dawn. Far too soon the sun would stand in the sky immovably hour after hour, burning with furnace-like power in the clear blue. Lissa always liked to spend that hour on the beach before it became overcrowded with holidaymakers.

This morning she felt stiff and tense, as though she had slept in a state of alarm all night. She slipped into one of her brief bikinis and put on a tiny white towelling robe. Fortuné scrambled after her as she made her way across the lawns towards the palms. The hotel was silent. The guests wouldn't be up for an hour or two at earliest. Many did not eat breakfast and only got up late in the morning, particularly those who played half the night in the casino.

On the beach Lissa dropped her robe and waded into the water, letting the warm swell of it carry her forward. The splash of Fortuné entering alongside her made her turn to grin at him. He bobbed along in her rear, paddling vigorously with his paws.

The sky this morning had a mild milky radiance. She swam for a while before turning on to her back to drift back to shore and was so absorbed by her thoughts that she did not notice the arrival on the beach until she came close enough to see and recognise him.

He was wearing sun-glasses, his face barred darkly by them, and they increased the faint threat she felt in him.

He stood on the pale sands, his hands on his hips, the short black swimming trunks belted low on his body, watching her as she uneasily walked out of the water.

'Good morning,' she said politely, smiling in a nervous manner.

'You get up early,' he observed, still staring. The mirror lenses flashed in the rising sun and made his face unreadable.

'Yes,' she said vaguely, looking round for her robe.

As she turned away Luc Ferrier remarked, 'I enjoyed your act last night. Clever.'

'Thank you.'

'Surprisingly so,' he added in a faint drawl which made her face grow pink. 'It wasn't what I'd been expecting.' Although she could not see the eyes behind their barrier, she felt them intensely as they swept over her. 'Particularly the dress. You're deceptive, Miss Radley.'

Lissa did not like the way he said that or the smile curling round his mouth as he said it.

She stood hesitantly, poised to go, and Luc Ferrier asked: 'What's the origin of the name Lissa? Unusual.'

'I was named Melissa,' she explained. 'But it was too long for me to say when I was little and Lissa stuck somehow.'

'Melissa,' he drawled, eyeing her. 'No, I don't like that. Lissa is much more suitable.'

She watched Fortuné gambolling like a saturated lamb, shaking himself clear of water which sprayed across the fine brittle sand in dark swirls.

'Well,' she stammered, 'enjoy your swim, Mr Ferrier.'

'Ah,' he said softly, 'you know my name.' She got a strange impression that that pleased him, for some reason. Did it give him a triumphant sensation to be recognised everywhere he went? When they had famous visitors at the hotel she had noticed that although they protested fiercely against their fame they were, all the same, irritated if they went unrecognised.

She was dying to ask him if he had played with Chris last night but felt hesitant to bring the subject up, as though it would reveal too much of her frame of mind to him.

From the first moment they met she had been strangely wary of him and as he watched her, her wariness increased.

'I'm in no hurry to swim,' he said. 'Sit and talk to me.'

Lissa looked at him in nervous alarm. 'Thank you, but I must get back to the hotel,' she said huskily.

'Why must you? Nobody is stirring yet,' he said. 'It's only seven o'clock.'

Lissa searched for some plausible reason, but took too long to do it. He took her elbow and pulled her down on the sand before she even knew his intention. Lissa looked at him with wide, troubled green eyes. If only he would take off those sun-glasses, she thought, staring at the arrogant nose and hard mouth.

As if he had heard her, he suddenly reached up and removed them. She looked unguardedly into the dark blue eyes and felt her stomach turn over without knowing why.

'How long have you worked at the hotel?' he asked.

'Since I left school.'

'When was that?' He smiled as he asked and the glint of amusement in his eyes deepened her flush.

'Two years ago,' she admitted.

'Which makes you?'

'Twenty,' she said.

His mouth twisted. 'Twenty,' he said on an odd, hard note. His blue eyes stared into hers intently. 'I'm thirty-seven,' he said as though she had asked, as though he was answering some unspoken question.

Lissa had no idea how to answer that, how to react. She looked away, nodding, her damp hair clinging to her damp shoulders as her head moved.

Fortuné was running along the pale sand, dancing on his own shadow. A seabird cried over his head and he looked up, barking, excited by the darting, daring flight.

She glanced back and her stomach turned over again as she found Luc Ferrier's blue eyes moving over her with a cool intensity which seemed to strip the few thin barriers between them from her body. Lissa drew a harsh breath and her blood ran fiercely up her neck and face.

His eyes lifted as if he had heard that intake of breath and he gave her a veiled smile.

'You're very lovely.'

She moved to rise and his hand clamped down on her arm, tethering her by his side.

'Where are you going?'

'I must go,' she muttered huskily.

She saw his black brows rise in that winged flight, mockery coming into the blue eyes. 'You're a funny mixture,' he commented. 'The quiet manner of a schoolgirl one minute and then when you came on to the stage last night you'd become a very sexy little package at a stroke. Is it your stage manner? Or do you reserve it for close acquaintances?'

Face burning, she said drily. 'Please let go of my arm, Mr Ferrier.'

He still stared at her, mockery in his face. His hand slid slowly, tantalisingly, down her arm and her skin tingled everywhere he touched.

'How do I register?' he asked, and she stared in bewilderment. 'As a close acquaintance?' he added to clarify the issue and Lissa was stiff with outrage at the tone he used.

He laughed at her flashing anger, her green eyes vivid in her suntanned face.

'Is there an entrance fee?'

'Let me go!' she snapped furiously, pulling free of him, and as she did so he caught sight of the handsome diamond glittering on her left hand. His fingers seized hers and he twisted her hand to bring it up into the sunlight.

'So,' he said curtly, 'you're engaged?'

'Yes,' she said with unhidden hostility.

'Who to?' he asked.

'Chris,' she said.

He was staring at the ring, his face totally expressionless. 'Chris?' He raised his dark blue eyes and Lissa could see no thought in them, only a cold blank fixity.

'Chris Brandon.'

His brow knitted. 'The hotel manager?'

'He owns the hotel.' She said that with a faint emphasis as though establishing Chris's status.

He dropped her hand and she rubbed it as though the grip of his powerful fingers had cramped the blood.

'How long have you been engaged? When's the wedding?' He sounded politely interested, and she could think of no reason for refusing to answer, although every fibre of her being was screaming out as though she were in some deadly danger. Lissa had never thought of herself as superstitious, yet something about Luc Ferrier raised the hair on the back of her neck. She could well understand why people called him Lucifer and said he was connected with the devil. She felt exactly the same herself.

'We've been engaged for a year,' she muttered.

'A year?' He asked that sharply as though eager to hear her answer.

Lissa looked at him in nervous impatience. 'Yes.'

He stared at her fixedly, the impassive lines of his features gleaming in the sunlight. The sun struck light from his tanned skin and turned it a brilliant gold, gave depth and power to the blue eyes, so that they pierced her and made her feel more and more alarmed. She felt he was looking right through her to her backbone, that he could read her mind as though her head was made of glass.

'And when's the wedding?' he asked in a slow, thoughtful voice.

Lissa slid her eyes from the compelling stare of his and mumbled, 'We haven't decided yet.'

He moved slightly and she looked at him in hurried wariness. He gave her a hard, cool smile. 'No hurry? How wise. One should never hurry into marriage. I'm sure the old saying is true—marry in haste, repent at leisure. I've borne it in mind all my life.' His smile was teasing, amused. 'I've no taste for repentance.'

Lissa could believe that. Looking at the sharp razor edges of his fleshless profile, she could easily believe it. Luc Ferrier wasn't a man who was likely to repent anything. She had the feeling he did just as he pleased and damn the consequences.

Looking away from him across the level sands, she asked huskily: 'Did you play last night, Mr Ferrier?'

'Of course,' he said, as though surprised she should ask. She felt him staring at her profile, the small soft outline of her face averted from him as far as possible. She had the features of a young girl, smooth-skinned and slightly delicate, her brow high and wide beneath the sleek wet blonde hair, her eyes set beneath thin brows, their slanting upward gleam hidden now by pale smooth lids fringed by darkened lashes which were naturally pale. Her nose was small and straight, her mouth tender. The rounded chin and long slender neck underlined her youth.

'Roulette?' she asked with dry nervousness.

'Poker,' he said, watching her.

She swallowed, trying to disguise it from him by keeping her face averted. 'Oh? Who did you play with?'

He was silent for a moment and she turned in a quick motion to look at him, meeting the sharp stab of his stare with alarm.

'Your fiancé,' he drawled, still watching her.

She tried to smile and it was a lamentable failure, her lips moving stiffly. 'I hope you didn't lose.'

Luc Ferrier's hard mouth twisted. 'Do you?' His eyes made it clear he did not believe that. 'Well, as it happens, I didn't.'

She fought not to show alarm, but his eyes narrowed as he watched her innocent, anxious face.

'Oh,' she said unevenly. 'Oh. Good.'

She rose and he rose with her. 'Well, I'd better have that swim,' he announced, to her relief. As she walked away she heard the splash of his entry into the water. The dog ran along ahead of her, prancing excitedly over the lawns which surrounded the hotel, delighted with his prolonged visit to the beach. A flock of birds soared up as he ran towards them, and Lissa's eyes followed their flight absently.

How much had Chris lost last night? Was he insane to play poker with a man whose face could put up shutters which hid every single thought in his head?

She showered and dressed and had a light breakfast of fruit and coffee. A few people were drifting through the foyer as she went towards the offices. They glanced at her in recognition as she passed them and she returned their smiling greetings.

'Hallo there,' one of them said, halting to detain her, his hand on her arm.

Lissa glanced up at him. She had seen him several times on the beach. He was not one of the gamblers; he was here for surfing and sunworship. His lithe brown body witnessed to that. At a guess she would say he was only a few years older than herself and from his manner she would imagine he had plenty of money. He was used to impressing the girls he dated. His light, shallow smile set her teeth on edge.

'Great act last night,' he told her. 'How about coming out for a drive with me this afternoon? Show me the island.' He gave her what he imagined would be an irresistible smile. 'We could have fun together.'

'My fiancé wouldn't like that,' Lissa said sweetly. She had had this sort of approach before from visitors. He was not going to be hard to deal with—he didn't have the dangerous control of Luc Ferrier. She found no difficulty in reading his mind at a glance. She smiled to herself. She might be alarmed by Luc Ferrier but men of this sort did not bother her an inch.

He looked disgruntled. 'Fiancé?'

'Chris Brandon,' she explained.

His hand dropped from her arm and he took a hurried step away. 'Oh.' She caught the incredulous, nervous flick of his eyes, then he was gone so fast it was laughable. Mention of Chris always seemed to make men sheer off fast. It was odd that Chris, for all his charm and lighthearted manner, somehow managed to have this effect on other men.

Although Chris employed a number of very tough

men from the back streets of the town, not one of them had ever so much as looked at Lissa with anything but careful courtesy. The hotel attracted a number of pretty girls. Lissa saw Chris's men around with some of these girls and recognised that their manner to other women bore no resemblance to the way they treated her. She found it touching. Chris's men knew that if they turned those insolent, appraising glances on her she would run like a rabbit, perhaps.

Or perhaps, she thought, as one of the men let her pass through into Chris's office with a careful smile, the men knew that Chris would get very angry if any of them as much as laid a finger on her.

He was having one of his morning conferences with the men who ran the casino. As Lissa walked into the room Chris was talking in a crisp, staccato fashion. She caught the tail-end of a sentence. 'Not a penny more. Got that?' Then Chris turned and saw her and his face softened and warmed. 'Good morning, darling.'

She walked over to kiss him while the men rose. Chris held her, his arm around her slender waist.

'We'll finish later,' he told his men, and they filed out, smiling at Lissa politely.

Max was the last to leave. She caught the white gleam of his teeth. Chris shot him a look and Max vanished.

Lissa looked up at Chris, frowning. 'How much did you lose last night?'

His eyes narrowed. 'Who told you I played?' She knew from the ring of his tone that he had warned his staff not to tell her and she looked at him crossly.

'Luc Ferrier himself!'

Chris stiffened. 'How did you come to meet him?'

'He was on the beach this morning. Chris, don't play

with him again. I don't trust him. He's too tough.'

She caught a flicker of something in his face, a shifting amusement, a brightness in his eyes. Sometimes Chris bothered her. She worried about that odd streak in him, the flaw which led him to run risks, to court danger.

'Honey, I'm in no danger,' he said softly. 'I only played to get his measure and I got out when I saw I was on a low streak. He's good, though. The best I've ever seen—he doesn't show a thing. And he gets the cards, my God he does! I watched him for another hour and his luck is unbelievable. I had Victor keep an eye on him in case he was a sharp, but Victor says not. He says it just isn't possible.'

'I hate gambling,' Lissa burst out. 'Chris, can't you close the casino? Go back to running a hotel and nothing else?'

Chris looked away, his mouth tight. 'No. The casino makes far too much money.'

'But, Chris——' she began, and he looked at her smilingly, his hand encompassing her waist and his fingers lightly resting on her midriff.

'Don't get excited, there's a good girl. The casino attracts most of our guests. If we closed down, someone else would open up and we would lose money hand over fist.'

She sighed. 'Well, promise not to play with Luc Ferrier again.'

'What do I get for being a good boy?' he asked coaxingly, smiling at her.

Lissa lifted her face and Chris's arms closed round her, pulling her towards him. His mouth closed hotly over her own and Lissa felt a curious little shiver of alarm. She often had it when Chris kissed her with that aroused heat. Something inside her backed away nervously from the passion he displayed when he held her.

'Liss, baby,' he groaned as he felt her faint withdrawal. 'You make my head spin. Kiss me properly, honey.'

There was a quick knock on the door. Chris's secretary, Rebecca, came into the room and Chris lifted his head to give her a sharp, angry look.

'Wait until I tell you to come in,' he rapped out.

Rebecca's face showed no reaction. She was a girl with a low, cool voice and an elegant, contained manner. She had worked for Chris for some years, running the office efficiently. When Chris teased Rebecca he got short shrift. She would look at him levelly and not smile, her face blank. Chris relied on her heavily, but Lissa sometimes got the impression that Rebecca was the one who ran the hotel, not Chris.

Sliding off Chris's lap, she walked to the door, giving Rebecca a quick smile. 'Sorry to break into the day's work.'

'There's a lot to do,' replied Rebecca. She always managed to make Lissa feel an intruder into the offices. She wasn't actually unfriendly, but she wasn't forthcoming either. She was neutral, a passive observer who yet gave the impression of doing more than merely observe.

'See you later, Chris,' said Lissa as she left.

'I can't wait, darling,' he said with a warm huskiness in his voice.

Lissa went off to rehearse with Pierre and the band for an hour or two and then went into town with a shopping list to fill. Joseph's wife Marie was the head housekeeper at the hotel. She and Joseph had a cabin in the grounds and a two-year-old baby called Lucien who spent his days with his grandmother down in Ville-Royale and only came up to join his parents at bedtime each day. Marie ran the housekeeping on a cheerful but efficient basis. Each of the girls had one floor in charge and Marie kept a stern eye on their activities.

Lissa came back in a taxi with her purchases and Marie smilingly thanked her. Lissa had done some shopping of her own. She unpacked her purchases in her own room and put them away tidily. She had had lunch at the tiny seafood restaurant on the quayside. It had been crowded with tourists who loved the lazy atmosphere of the old harbour.

The heat was now oppressive. She folded back the stiff honeycomb weave cover and lay down on the bed for an hour. She felt sleepy and weary, but as soon as her eyes closed she knew she wouldn't sleep. She was too busy worrying about Chris and Luc Ferrier. Would Chris keep his word? Normally he kept his promises to her, but where gambling was concerned Chris was unreliable.

It was her basic reason for not marrying him yet. She did not feel she could quite trust him. A man who has an addiction can't be trusted. He is an unstable element, dangerous, volatile, and has to be handled with care. Lissa knew that. She had watched Chris for years and she knew he was flawed right down the middle. The charm and warmth and kindness she loved could not hide from her the weak streak in him.

That evening she and Chris strolled down through the gardens in the twilight which within a few moments would become night. The sun went down with a rush as though swallowed by the sea, dragged by a hook into the jaws of a giant fish, the natives said. Each morning the fish spat it out and it shot into the sky in burning splendour to burn there for hour after hour unchanging until abruptly it was pulled back into the fish again.

The air was as warm as if the sun still hung above them. The sky was darkening to a soft purple. The sound of the surf came through the palms and the night was scented by honeysuckle whose perfumed sweetness filled the nostrils and almost made one suffocate. It grew in great profusion, the long stamens like yellow tongues, and orchids massed below it. Natives to the island and growing wild in the shadowy creeper-draped forest, their thick gaudy flesh was distasteful to Lissa.

On the edge of the palm-fringed beach Chris paused, his arm round her back, and looked across the dark ocean. 'Peaceful, isn't it?'

'Yes,' she said, leaning her head on his shoulder and wishing she felt peaceful but knowing she didn't.

Chris turned her to face him, his hands on her shoulders. She looked up and his face looked different in the smoky light. An alien excitement made his eyes glitter and his mouth taut.

'Liss,' he muttered, bending his head.

His mouth closed over hers and his arms held her tightly. She felt his hands begin to move up and down her back. He kissed her in a way he had never kissed her before, harder, more determined. His hands were gripping and clutching her and Lissa was torn between yielding and struggling.

A sound disturbed Chris's absorbed concentration

on her. He slowly lifted his head and glanced over his shoulder into the shadows behind them. Lissa looked that way too, but saw nothing. The darkness hid whatever moved in it.

'Marry me now, Liss,' Chris muttered, turning back to her in a fierce movement. 'For your own sake, baby, because my patience is wearing thin, and if we don't get married soon I'm going to do something we'll both regret. I'm not superhuman and I can't take much more of this.'

She leaned her head on his chest, her arms going round him. 'Yes,' she whispered unsteadily, although her head was choked with doubts. Chris wasn't a safe bet for anyone, but she loved him, and what was she to do? Unstable, addicted though he might be, he was still Chris and she had loved him all her life. She was going to have to take him as she found him. Chris had always been loving and kind to her. She was well aware that many men who were in love with a girl wouldn't be prepared to wait month after month as Chris had done. It hadn't been through any lack of passion that he had waited. At times she found it very impressive that he should be ready to wait when she could feel the impatient desire mounting inside him.

Now his hands held her tightly, he breathed into her hair, his heart racing violently. 'Liss darling, I want you so badly it's tearing me apart.'

She heard again a faint rustling behind them. Wakeful birds? she thought. Or one of the hotel cats on the prowl?

Chris was running his hands down her back and he was trembling. 'My God, you turn me on Liss!'

She felt a fierce colour run into her face at the voice,

the look in his eyes. Chris frightened her when he looked at her like that. She half backed, biting her lip.

He stared at her, his mouth a tight line. 'Okay, I'm not going to press you tonight,' he said thickly. 'But for the love of God, grow up. I've used kid gloves with you for months. You say you love me, but you keep putting things off. I'm not asking for the moon, am I? I want to marry you, not just take you to bed.' His face softened from the harsh lines. 'Liss, I love you, darling. Trust me. Let's get married soon.'

She was relieved by the reappearance of his smile. When Chris had that liquid heat in his eyes she felt threatened, uneasy. She did not know him when he looked like that. It was one of the reasons why she felt she couldn't commit herself to him.

Huskily she whispered, 'We'd better walk back—I've got to go on and do my act, remember.'

Chris made a twisted face, his hands dropping away from her. 'Okay.' They turned back towards the close-packed palm trees and as they walked through them they heard footsteps and saw a red flare. The scent of cigar smoke drifted to them.

Chris glanced through the darkness quickly and Lissa felt her heart wince in a strange little spasm.

'Good evening,' said Luc Ferrier in a lazy, deep voice. 'Romantic down here by moonlight, isn't it?'

'Taking a walk before settling to the tables?' Chris asked lightly giving him a smile.

A shiver was running down Lissa's back. She remembered the faint movements she had heard while she and Chris were on the beach and as she met Luc Ferrier's guarded, unreadable eyes she had a distinct flash of warning. Luc Ferrier had been watching her and Chris, listening to them. She did not know what told her that; it was a certainty which she felt as the hard blue eyes glanced over her and moved back to Chris.

'Are we going to hear that clever little song again to-night, Miss Radley?' Luc Ferrier drawled, smiling in a way she did not like.

She flushed. 'No.'

'Pity,' he remarked, and Chris's hand enclosed her waist and drew her close to him in a possessive movement. He nodded to Luc Ferrier and they walked on in silence. Lissa did not know what was absorbing Chris's mind, but she was relieved not to have to talk.

She did her usual act that night and was aware of the disappointment of the audience, although they applauded goodhumouredly enough as she bowed. She had aroused their expectations last night and they were far less enthusiastic now.

Luc Ferrier was at his table again. Lissa shot him a hurried look and saw his dark head veiled in drifting smoke. A cigar glowed red in the shadows around him.

She felt oddly nervous as she went off. Chris was no-where in sight and she kept her fingers crossed as she walked through to the foyer on her way to bed. He would be in the rooms, of course, but with any luck he would keep his promise with her own promise in mind. If he was really as desperate to marry her as he said he was, he wouldn't ruin it by gambling with that man again.

Fortuné was at the desk with the night clerk. Lissa picked him up and rubbed his rough head. 'Been for a walk?' she asked.

'I didn't get no time, Miss Lissa,' the clerk apologised. 'Sorry, but we've been very busy.'

'I'll take him,' she said, smiling. 'I could do with some air.'

Moonlight lay in wide silver lakes across the grounds, turning the leaves of trees into looking-glasses and sheeting the grass with pale light.

Lissa put Fortuné down and he scampered away excitedly as he caught sight of a small thin shadow slipping away. One of the hotel cats, she realised, whistling the dog. Fortuné kept going, growling in the back of his throat.

Making a face, Lissa followed him through the close-set trees. The scent of the honeysuckle drifted to her and she inhaled it with a sigh.

She heard a footstep behind her and turned abruptly. A tall, dark figure emerged from the sheltering gloom around it, and her heart stopped with a fierce pang.

Her mouth dried up. She felt like running, which was absurd, because what did she think he might do? There were plenty of people within earshot and she only had to scream if he so much as laid a finger on her.

'Where are you going?' he asked lazily, sauntering towards her, the moonlight checkering his body and giving him the appearance of a harlequin, the black hair a neat cap.

'I'm taking my dog for a walk,' she said huskily, furious with herself for her own nervous reaction to him.

He came closer. She saw the blue eyes glinting in the moonlight, as though he could read the panic which had flared up in her and was amused by it.

'Your act tonight was more what I'd expected from you,' he told her softly.

Lissa prickled with annoyance at that, and a flush

ran up her face. 'I'm glad you were pleased,' she said in a brittle voice.

He laughed, watching her with wicked amusement. Lissa turned to go on an impulse of sheer fury and he caught her arm.

'Don't move,' he said, as though warning her against some danger.

'Why?' she asked, startled.

'I want to watch the moonlight sliding down your throat and between your breasts,' he murmured, smiling, and Lissa's nerves leapt with angry fire.

She pushed his hand away and turned on her heel. The insolence of his tone was not making her as angry as her own reaction to the look in the teasing blue eyes. Her spine had shivered as he stared at her like that.

As she walked away Luc Ferrier said softly, 'Lucky moonlight,' and although Lissa struggled to retain command of herself she was so alarmed that she broke into a run. She heard him laughing and could have burst into tears of humiliation.

CHAPTER THREE

CHRIS was terse and irritable next day. When he snapped at her Lissa looked at him in anxious surprise and he turned away, his shoulders set.

'Did you play last night?' she asked hurriedly, and he gave her a furious look.

'No, I didn't. I promised, didn't I?'

Relief flooded into her and she understood the reason for his mood. Chris had kept his word, but it had been a hard struggle. He was feeling cross with her for demanding that promise. At least, though, he had won his fight against himself. Against himself—and against Luc Ferrier, she thought sinkingly.

She had not slept well again. Her dreams, when she had them, had been dappled with moonlight, which wasn't so surprising, since the moon lay all night in the room and passed over her sleeping face like a caressing, curious hand. In the dream moonlight Lissa was in flight from a faceless pursuing figure, a harlequin, silent and laughing at the same time. She did not once look over her shoulder, but she could feel him there and burning panic ran in her veins.

Whenever she had had problems as a child she had taken them away from the hotel to brood over them in private far away from everyone. Her favourite bolthole had been the echoing, creeper-hung forest which crept down towards the hotel from the hills.

The edge of it was penetrable, crowded with tall

palms and banana trees, locust trees among whose branches gleamed the brilliant plumage of tropical birds. She rarely saw anyone there.

When she had left Chris sulkily at work she whistled for Fortuné and walked out of the hotel grounds, cutting along the narrow dirt track road which lay close beside the forest. The dog vanished on one of his own expeditions and Lissa moved off the track into the deep green of the forest.

The grass was thick and coarse, a vivid green, with flowers sprinkled among it. A little stream ran beneath the trees down from the hills. The stony bed of it could be seen clearly through the crystal clear water. Sunlight glanced through the foliage and sparkled on tiny quartz stones on the stream bottom. Lissa was wearing a pair of her brief denim shorts. She kicked off her straw sandals and waded into the stream. The water was cool, icy when it first left the hills but warming as it ran down to the sea. A gnarled willow hung over the water, and Lissa pulled a leaf from it, the long serrated edge almost cutting her palm, and stirred the water with it like a child.

There was a movement among the trees. Startled, she looked up, and the willow leaf fell from her hand and drifted, swirling, down the stream.

Her heart beat a rapid tattoo as the black-haired figure moved towards her.

'How old did you say you were?' Luc Ferrier asked drily, staring at her long brown legs, the stream washing softly round them. The hem of her shorts was dark with splashed water. Her hair shone golden in the sunlight glancing through the trees.

It was more than a coincidence that he was there and

Lissa knew it, her instincts prickling.

'You followed me!' she accused.

He leaned on the low branch of the willow, his long lean body as briefly clad as her own in shorts and a sleeveless black cotton top.

'Clever,' he mocked, eyeing her with amusement.

Last night he had flung her into panic and confusion, but this morning it was daylight and she did not intend to let him bother her again. She lifted her rounded chin defiantly and glared at him, the green eyes very sharp and cold.

'I don't know what's in your mind, Mr Ferrier ...'

'Oh, yes, you do,' he drawled, a wicked light in his eyes.

Her flush deepened, but she obstinately went on with her little speech. 'But I'm not interested.'

'Sleep well last night?' he asked softly, and their eyes clashed before Lissa could look away. She felt the probe of his stare intensely. He slowly moved his eyes and looked at her throat. The tiny blue vein visible beneath her skin began to beat faster than ever. Lissa struggled to get a grip on herself; bewildered, deeply disturbed. She didn't even like him. He frightened her. Why was she trembling like this?

He moved, the water lapping round his bare legs, and she looked at him, eyes wide and nervous. He was a head taller, his shoulders very broad under the black cotton. The throat of it lay open, and sunlight flickered over his brown skin. Lissa looked at the powerful muscled strength of his body and her heart was in her throat.

She had never thought of herself as particularly superstitious, but she was feeling a primitive, superstitious dread now, an instinct older than time, buried deep in the back of her subconscious. Slender and dry-mouthed, she looked back at Luc Ferrier and felt a pressing urge to run, to hide. She had never in her life been so conscious of being a woman. She had grown up sheltered and protected by the men around her. Even Chris kept a strong hold over his own feelings around her. Now she felt her own femininity and, in contrast, the strong threat of this man's masculinity, and she hadn't got a clue how to deal with him except by running.

As if he understood exactly how she felt he was watching her with a strange little smile, his winged black brows rising. 'My God,' he drawled, 'you show everything, don't you?'

Her flush deepened, her eyes widened further.

'You shouldn't be allowed out on your own,' he added with a mixture of amusement and wryness. 'It's time you learnt to hide your feelings.'

'I don't know what you're talking about,' she muttered huskily, head bent.

'You know precisely what I'm talking about,' he said with a smile in his voice. 'I wouldn't be here if you didn't.'

That ambiguous remark quickened her heart and intensified her state of nervous tension. He was close, far too close, the strength of his tall body an increasing threat the closer he came. The cotton shirt rose and fell as he breathed and she watched it, staring at the muscled structure of his chest beneath it.

A flash of startling blue winged over the stream and they both glanced round as a bird vanished into the close-set trees behind them. 'Fascinating,' Luc Ferrier said. 'The colours here make the eyes ache.'

'You haven't been here before?'

He turned his head towards her, the strong brown throat catching her eye, and smiled down at her. 'No, my first time. I'm impressed, but in five years' time the place will be ruined. You can see the signs everywhere. Once tourists start flocking in, everything changes.'

Lissa sighed. 'I'm afraid you're probably right.'

'Your fiancé's casino has started the rot,' he informed her.

'You wouldn't be here if the casino wasn't here,' Lissa counter-attacked sharply.

He inclined his head. 'True. That doesn't stop me seeing that the march of progress doesn't always make for happiness. The islanders are still able to enjoy life in their own way, but once foreigners flood in with more money than most of the natives have ever seen and a way of life they never dreamt about, discontent and resentment will spread like wildfire.'

Lissa had no argument with that point of view. She had seen the beginning of it already in Ville-Royale. But for some reason she bristled when Luc Ferrier said what she had thought herself. She looked at him sharply, her green eyes dagger-bright.

'It depends on their sense of values.'

'Values have to be pretty strong to stand up to a dose of modern Westernised living,' he drawled, watching the angry gleam of her eyes.

'If you disapprove of that sort of world why do you go from casino to casino gambling?' she asked contemptuously.

His blue eyes held a mixture of laughter and odd appraisal. 'That's what I am,' he shrugged, 'a gambler. That's how I live.'

'Surely you could live some other way? It can't be a very pleasant life. You can't win all the time.' Lissa looked at the powerful body, the compelling blue eyes, the fierce bone structure of his face, and frowned. He did not look like a man with a weakness. You could read the flaw in Chris by merely looking into his restless eyes. He couldn't hide it because it weakened the whole fibre of his nature. But Luc Ferrier betrayed no such weakness. It wasn't merely that he was physically strong—there was a lazy, certain strength in his eyes. He was aware of himself, of everything around him, and sure of his own ability to face and defeat anything that barred his path.

He was smiling slightly, a mocking twist of the lips which held a faint grimness. 'Ah, but I do,' he told her. 'I never lose. Now and then I have a temporary problem, some resistance, but in the end I always get what I want.'

She met the direct, watchful gleam of the blue eyes and her nerve ends rang wild alarm bells. Looking away hurriedly, she looked round. 'I wonder where Fortuné has got to.' She called him loudly and got no answer. All was silence.

Luc Ferrier whistled on a long, high note and she heard the crashing through undergrowth of the dog making his way towards them.

Luc glanced down at her, grinning. 'He's coming.'

She sensed his amusement and her eyes grew more annoyed. 'He couldn't have heard me,' she said, because she was not going to admit that her dog had ignored her but come to that man's whistle.

The white body hurled itself through the stream, but as Lissa turned to catch him, Fortuné flung himself at Luc Ferrier, barking excitedly, in welcome and recognition, his pink tongue lolling. Luc bent and picked him up, squirming. Holding him away, he said in mock sternness: 'And where have you been? You're filthy, you horrible animal!'

She saw he was right. The dog's white coat was smeared with sand and mud, his paws black.

Luc lowered the dog and deliberately immersed him in the water, rubbing his coat and paws to clean them. Fortuné struggled and barked, but was helpless in the firm grip.

'Now you look better,' said Luc, releasing him.

Fortuné sat down in the water, his head just above it, and scratched himself energetically.

Luc laughed. 'He's an adventurous little beast, isn't he?' His blue eyes lifted and Lissa met them. 'Unlike his owner,' he added softly.

She pretended she had not heard that. Moving away, the water gently flowing round her bare legs, she told Fortuné to come along. Luc walked after her and watched her step into her straw sandals.

He moved away to get his own. Lissa hurried away, the dog running before her, hoping to get back to the hotel before Luc Ferrier had caught up with her, but he was behind her a moment later, the long strides of his brown legs covering the ground at an enormous pace.

'I haven't had a chance to see the island yet,' he told her. 'What is there to do here?'

'Very little,' she hedged.

'Where do you go apart from the hotel?' he pressed.

'Into town,' she said.

'To do what?'

'Shop. Have you seen the old fort yet? If you're interested in that sort of thing it's worth seeing.'

'Show it to me this afternoon,' he came back at once.

Lissa stiffened. 'I'm afraid ...'

'No?' He stopped her before her stammered excuse came out, shrugging with casual indifference. 'Never mind, I'll find someone else to show it to me. I thought you could fill me in on the history of the island.'

'I have to work,' Lissa said nervously, not wishing to sound rude yet wanting to make it clear to him that she was not spending any time with him. 'I'm sorry,' she added, to pretend he was merely another visitor, trying to cover from him her instinctive wariness of him.

'You don't come into the gaming rooms,' he commented, watching her. 'Don't you like gambling?'

'No.' Lissa did not enlarge on that, her small face stiff.

'Your fiancé likes it.' He said that coolly, eyes sharp.

She knew he would not miss the faint tremor that ran over her, but she could do nothing to control it. She gave him no answer, walking faster.

'He's got the bug badly,' Luc Ferrier drawled, still watchful. 'You shouldn't let him play. He hasn't got the face for it.'

'You don't have to play with him,' she accused in an uneven voice.

'I don't have to play with anyone,' he agreed. 'I choose who I play against.' He paused and added very softly, 'And why.'

She stopped in her tracks and looked round, shaken and disturbed by that voice, those words.

He met her eyes directly. He wasn't smiling and his eyes were a cool, glinting blue.

'Why do you play with Chris?' she asked huskily, hoping he couldn't see the faint dew which had sprung out on her upper lip and forehead.

'He has something I want,' Luc Ferrier said, and her stomach cramped as though clenched in agony.

Trying to breathe evenly, she asked in a shaky voice, 'What?'

She saw the slow derisive lift of his dark brows, the sardonic twist of his mouth. 'I don't have to tell you that, do I, Lissa?'

She swallowed. 'Money?' she whispered, and he laughed under his breath.

'Money? I never gamble for money.'

The answer took her breath away. She stared in total disbelief. He grinned, amused by her amazement.

'Gamblers never do—real gamblers, that is—oh, the amateurs may do it for that, but then it's the money they're interested in, not the gambling.' He had a reckless, vital amusement in his face. 'A real gambler does it for the sheer hell of it. The kick he gets when he has a big win. The danger, the uncertainty, the knowledge that he's walking a tightrope over an abyss without a safety net.' He paused and smiled oddly at her. 'Ask your fiancé. He doesn't gamble for money, either. He gambles for the same reason as myself—he has an urge to prove himself against other men.' His eyes glittered like strange blue stones and his skin was taut. 'He wants to flatten me.'

She remembered Chris saying excitedly: 'I can take

him,' and the feverish brightness of his eyes. 'Why does he want to beat you so much?' she asked Luc Ferrier with unhidden anxiety.

He shrugged wryly. 'I've got a reputation, I suppose. It gets around, and men hanker for the thrill of being able to say they beat me. It can be irritating. Every place I go to there's going to be someone itching to take me and wring me dry. Not for the money—just for the boosted ego of doing it.'

Lissa was worried and angry and she burst out furiously: 'Why do you go on living like that? Drifting around from casino to casino, winning and losing money day after day. It's degrading!'

'I only gamble in the summer,' he said with wicked amusement. 'The rest of the year I risk my life in London traffic.'

She frowned. 'What?'

He was mocking her. 'I suppose it's another form of gambling, really.'

'What are you talking about?'

'My job,' he said, and Lissa's mouth opened on a surprised intake of air.

Luc laughed again. 'Close your mouth. Are you catching flies? Out here you might catch something much nastier.'

'Job?' she repeated huskily.

'Nasty word, isn't it?' he said. 'I try to keep it quiet. It only confuses people.'

'You work?'

His laughter deepened and he bent a wicked eye on her. 'Alas, yes.'

'What at?' she asked, unable to believe he meant it.

'What a narrow-minded girl you are!' he drawled. 'I

work in a London office for nine months of the year, actually.'

'Doing what?' Lissa regarded him incredulously.

'Gambling,' he mocked, grinning.

Lissa's teeth set. 'I don't believe you!' He was making fun of her. She turned to go and he caught her arm, his fingers folding softly round her elbow, not hurting yet making it impossible for her to move away.

'I work with the Stock Exchange,' he explained.

'The London Stock Exchange?'

'That's right. I gamble on market fluctuations. I'm good at it, I make a lot of money. It calls for the same skills as poker. You have to have intuition, a gut feeling that some stock is about to move up or down, and the nerve to back your judgment with hard cash. In the last resort, that's what all gambling comes to—nerve and a clear head.' He paused, eyeing her. 'That's why your fiancé should stay away from it. He has the nerve and the desire to win, but he doesn't have the head for it.'

Lissa looked at the hard, assertive face and swallowed. 'Don't play with him again!' The fear she was feeling was inexplicable. All her instincts cried out that for Chris to play against Luc Ferrier was dangerous. She couldn't say why she should feel that. It was an unconscious reaction deep inside her and her conscious mind couldn't pin down the hidden reasoning which had caused it.

Luc Ferrier's blue eyes narrowed and he watched her closely. 'We'll make a bargain,' he told her.

'What?' She looked anxiously into the blue eyes, her face shifting in uncertainty.

'Spend the afternoon with me and I promise I won't

play poker with your fiancé tonight,' he drawled.

Lissa sensed at once that he had led her into that trap deliberately. He had known she was nervous about Chris playing with him and he had played on her fears.

'Well?' he demanded.

She looked down, biting her lower lip, trying to think. It was blatant blackmail and she would need her head examined if she gave in to it. Chris had promised he wouldn't play with Luc Ferrier, hadn't he? But Chris was a gambler and Lissa knew gamblers. Chris would forget his promise to her if his passion for poker beckoned.

Luc Ferrier turned away, shrugging those wide shoulders. 'Okay, forget it. Obviously you have no objections to Brandon playing with me, after all.'

'I'll come,' she said huskily as he moved away.

He stopped and turned. The blue eyes smiled and she caught her breath at the beauty of them, set in their thick black lashes, the compelling nature of that smile irresistible.

She knew it was madness to agree to spend the afternoon with him, but if she had refused she guessed he would have persuaded Chris to play tonight and Chris would have lost again. Lissa was certain of it. Chris hadn't got a hope against Luc Ferrier.

She left Fortuné at the desk with the day clerk and went to her room. She showered and changed into a plain blue shift in glazed cotton. It was sleeveless, with a low scooped neckline, quite short, exposing most of her body to the sun. Brushing her long blonde hair, she thought about the problem facing her. How was she going to spend several hours with Luc Ferrier and still keep him at a safe distance? In the past her innocence had protected her. All the men who worked at the hotel kept their distance without her having to do anything about it. They might smile, eye her admiringly, but they had never stepped over the line they drew for themselves.

She did not need to guess that Luc Ferrier was going to be much tougher to handle; everything about him made it blazingly obvious.

She drew her hair behind her head and anchored it with a small black velvet bow. The change of hairstyle gave her face a pure outline, very young, very innocent. She regarded herself assessingly. Yes, she decided, that was better. She did not put on any make-up. Quite often in the summer she didn't bother. Her tanned skin did not need it and spending so much time in the ocean she just forgot to put make-up on except in the evenings when she was going to work.

When she joined Luc Ferrier she felt the quick, all-seeing shaft of his glance. The blue eyes were sardonic as she looked up into them. He knew she had dressed carefully and deliberately and he knew why.

'Very demure,' he murmured softly. 'Sweet and innocent. You look like a daisy.'

She flushed, not liking the comparison.

'Shall we be on our way?' Luc asked, and she turned reluctantly to walk out with him.

Rebecca was crossing the foyer with a clipboard and sheaf of papers in her hand. Lissa felt her staring and avoided her eyes. Rebecca would tell Chris, she realised with a quiver of alarm. What would Chris say when he found out she had gone off with Luc Ferrier?

She took Luc to the best restaurant in town. It did not look much on the outside. Housed in one of the frame buildings on the front, it had a ramshackle air, leaning crazily in the wind, creaking like an old boat. Inside it was elegantly furnished and the food was superb. It was island cooking at its best—tinged with that distinct French flavour which centuries of French dominance had given the islanders. The ingredients were alien, but the cooking and serving gave the meal a classic simplicity.

'What's in this sauce?' Luc asked her, looking with pleasure at his plate.

'Local honey, spices, pineapple, vinegar,' she said. He was eating octopus with rice and baked bananas. His brows had risen as he read the menu, but she could see that he was enjoying the odd combination and Lissa knew from experience that it was delicious.

She herself was eating chicken sliced very thinly and served wrapped in slices of local molasses-cooked ham.

Their waiter knew her and hovered politely within earshot—she wasn't sure whether he did it out of a desire to be some sort of protection for her, or whether he was merely eager to please. Whenever she looked round she caught the white flash of his teeth as he smiled at her.

Luc saw her smiling back and glanced over his broad shoulder. He crooked a long, brown finger and the waiter sprang forward. 'Sir?'

'If we want you, we'll call you,' Luc said very softly, meeting his eyes.

The waiter bowed and silently vanished.

'They all know you, don't they?' Luc asked, and Lissa nodded, smiling faintly.

'How old were you when you first came here?'

She told him and he listened with interest. 'So you were born in England?'

She nodded, and he pushed away his plate and leaned back in his chair, his thumbs in the pockets of the waistcoat of his light blue suit. It was one of the things about him that betrayed his money—the cut of the suit had London stamped all over it. The design was modern without being aggressively in fashion and the tailoring was first class. He wasn't wearing a tie and the collar of his shirt was casually opened.

'Have you ever wanted to go back to England?' he asked, studying her coolly.

Lissa shook her head. 'Not to live—for a visit, perhaps. I think I'd find it a bit cold.'

He lowered his thick lashes. 'Not necessarily,' he answered, and she saw the edge of his mouth curl upwards in a secret little smile.

Glancing up again, he asked: 'So you've known Brandon most of your life?'

Lissa nodded. She felt his eyes probing into hers, the razor-sharp edge of his face tilted as he leaned back.

'What gave you the idea you could sing?' he asked, and she didn't like the way he phrased that, flushing.

'Chris thought ...'

'Ah,' he said. 'It was his idea, was it?'

'I know I'm not the greatest singer in the world!' she flared in defensive annoyance.

'You're not even in the third league,' he drawled.

Her colour deepened. 'Thank you.'

He grinned at her stiff voice and angry face. 'But you're worth listening to,' he soothed. 'That little girl voice is rather fetching. You're such a contrast to the sort of singers you usually find in places like that.' He watched her push her own plate away, only half-touched, and asked: 'Would you like a dessert?'

She shook her head, her eyes down. Although she knew she wasn't a very exciting singer she did not much like being frankly informed of it.

'Coffee?' He didn't wait for her to answer that, but clicked his fingers. The waiter appeared and Luc ordered coffee. When their plates had been removed he asked if she would mind if he smoked and, when she shook her head, he lit a cigar.

'The song you sang the other night,' he began, studying the end of his cigar thoughtfully. 'Whose idea was that?'

'Pierre's,' she said. 'He runs the band. He arranged the song and did the modern words.'

The dark blue eyes shot to her face. 'You weren't happy singing it, were you? You got through it okay, but you looked like someone who was in acute discomfort.'

Lissa did not answer that. The waiter arrived with their coffee and left the tall pot of coffee on the table when he vanished again to get the brandy Luc had demanded for himself.

Lissa watched the pale spirals of cream sink into her coffee. Luc watched her, but he wasn't saying anything. The brandy arrived and when the waiter had gone again Luc picked up his glass and sipped the drink in silence for a moment.

'Girls of your type have gone out of style in England,' he told her as he put his glass down on the table.

Lissa ventured a look at him and flushed at the wicked amusement in his eyes.

'What do you mean, girls of my type?' she asked crossly. 'What type am I?'

'I haven't got long enough to tell you,' he said softly, and her colour flared.

She picked up her coffee and drank it to cover her disturbed sense of threat. The way the blue eyes caressed and teased made her want to get up and bolt like a frightened rabbit.

She was very relieved when they had finished their coffee and could leave. It would be less intimate and more bearable for her when they were viewing the old fort, she decided, but when they strolled down the road and went in through the open gate they found the place empty. The young man selling tickets waved them through cheerfully. 'You know the way round, Liss,' he beamed.

The walls were broken in places, the jagged masonry worn by wind and sea mists, the ground littered with tumbled stone. Lissa showed Luc the guardrooms with their deepset chimneys, the cells beneath the fort which had once held chained prisoners, the narrow winding corridors running darkly off the steep flights of stairs. A colony of bats lived in the ruined tower at one end of the fort. Luc insisted on climbing the stairs to stare down over the town from the wide parapet. Long ago French soldiers had stood here, watching for trouble either from land or sea, but the fort had not been in use for many years.

The wind blew faintly today. In summer the town sweltered in the heat. It was only when the occasional hurricane roared over the ocean that the fort crumbled even further.

Going down the stairs with Luc in front of her in case

she fell, Lissa skidded on a sharply polished stone. She tried to grab the wall, but it gave her hand no purchase. Instead she found herself grasping Luc's shoulders while he held her by the waist, half turned towards her in a reflex movement as he heard her cry of alarm.

'Sorry,' she whispered, drawing back as she recovered her balance.

He still held her waist, his hands almost meeting around it, and as she looked into his eyes a strange, drowning excitement engulfed her. Her mind blanked out. When Luc lifted her down to the same step as himself she felt she was floating, light as air, dreamlike and somehow free of anything resembling volition.

Luc's head bent and he brushed his lips over hers. It was the lightest of caresses and it affected her like the touch of fire. She jerked back involuntarily. The cold stone of the wall, the rough edge of flint, dug into her back. She stared into his intent blue eyes and her mouth shook.

He placed both hands on the wall, leaning over her, and his mouth came down again, but now the coolness had gone, along with the gentleness. His lips were hard and hot, forcing hers to open, the pressure of them filled with a demand she helplessly obeyed. His hands suddenly gripped her wrists and raised her arms, placing them round his neck. She woke briefly then, wrenching her head away, pushing at his shoulders with flattened hands.

His palm against her cheek pushed her head round and before she could cry out in protest his mouth had her own captive again. Lissa tensed for a few seconds, twisting to escape. Luc shifted and she felt the whole weight of his body crushing her against the wall. She couldn't stop the moan which escaped her under his demanding mouth. Her hands slid along his shoulders and grasped his thick black hair, running through it in a trembling movement.

Luc broke off the kiss to lift his head. Her lids flicked back and her green eyes stared, glazed and incredulous.

She felt the piercing probe of those eyes with heated embarrassment and self-disgust.

Luc stepped away, smiling. 'Be more careful as we go down the rest of these stairs,' he drawled. 'You never know what may happen if you slip.'

Lissa couldn't move for a moment. Her legs were shaking under her and she was so hot she felt as though she had a fever. After a pause to drag herself back from that disturbed state of consciousness, she followed him slowly.

CHAPTER FOUR

CHRIS was in the foyer when they got back to the hotel. He was talking to the desk clerk with his back towards them, but at the sound of Luc Ferrier's cool voice he swung and looked across the empty foyer at them, a spot of red burning in each cheek. Chris was angry. Lissa saw the fury in him and stiffened in alarm. Luc sauntered away, a smile on his hard mouth, and she slowly walked towards Chris.

He didn't say a word. He took her elbow and marched her into his office, slamming the door in Rebecca's face as she watched them.

Swinging on Lissa, Chris asked tightly: 'Okay, why did you go off with him, and where the hell have you been? You've been gone most of the afternoon.'

'He asked me to show him the fort,' Lissa began.

'He what?' Chris reacted with outright fury, his flush deepening. 'He wasn't interested in any forts!'

Meeting his blue eyes, she swallowed, and Chris watched the movement of her throat, his face hard.

'What happened?' he demanded, keeping his eyes fixed on her. 'And I want the truth, the whole truth and nothing but the truth, Liss!'

'He said if I went with him he wouldn't play with you,' she confessed, and Chris looked at her in fierce stupefaction.

'I was quite safe in daylight,' she began, but Chris wasn't even listening.

'You actually bargained with him about it?'

'I was worried——' she began, and he cut her short with a loud, harsh expletive.

'You talked to him about it? You discussed me with him? Told him you were worried in case I played with him?' He used words he had never used before in her presence and the charm and warmth was stripped from his face as though it had never been present. She did not know him. The hoarse tone of his voice frightened her.

He grabbed her shoulders, his fingers digging into her, and shook her. 'You stupid little bitch,' he hissed. 'Do you know what you've done? Have you any idea? My God, I could slap your damned face for you!'

Lissa shrank, trembling, looking at him with wide and horrified eyes.

'He'll use every tiny scrap you fed him,' Chris bit out. 'You just tossed me into the jaws of a crocodile, you little bitch ...'

'Don't,' she winced as his cruel fingers clenched on her. 'You're hurting!'

Tears burst into her eyes, partly of pain from the way he was shaking her, partly from misery because he was so angry. Chris stared at her as the drops slid down her cheek, and she felt the rage in him die out. He drew a long breath and then sighed deeply.

'Okay,' he muttered, drawing her into his arms. His lips brushed the top of her head. 'Don't cry, honey baby. Liss, stop crying. I can't stand to hear you cry like that.'

She had never seen him so angry before. The brutal, violent face he had shown her was a face she did not recognise. She was so shaken that she trembled in his arms and Chris groaned under his breath.

'Okay, it's okay, Liss. I realise you were only trying to save me from myself.' There was a peculiar smile in his voice, a secret amusement she didn't understand. He put a hand under her chin and pushed back her head. Wet-eyed, she gazed up at him, and Chris brushed his lips lightly across her trembling mouth.

'I told you I wouldn't gamble with him!'

'Then why were you so angry?'

She caught a wary flicker in his eyes. He looked away as she watched him.

'If you aren't going to gamble with him, why should it matter what I said to him?' she insisted, staring at him.

An odd little shiver ran down her spine as she observed the shadow of some secret thought passing through his face. She had known Chris most of her life, but what did she really know about the man behind that handsome face?

Chris's charm and easy smile didn't quite add up, and she had never realised it before. Even now she couldn't be certain what it was about him that was disturbing her. She had thought it was his urgent desire for her that made her hang back in nervous wariness, but behind her innocence she was intelligent enough to receive faint, puzzling signals from the atmosphere here in the island, fleeting indications that all was not what it seemed. Chris disturbed her, but she could not be sure why.

'Why were you so angry?' she pressed, and Chris gave her a casual, impatient grin.

'You never know—I might come up against him some day and I wouldn't want him to know too much about me. You shouldn't have let him see you were afraid he'd beat me. It's too revealing.'

'What difference does it make what I think?' Lissa asked, frowning as she watched him.

Chris's mouth twisted. 'You could have picked it up from me,' he grimaced. 'This man is like a radar system, he picks up every tiny signal. If he reckons I'm scared of him that will give him an advantage.'

'Don't play with him,' she said huskily. She paused, 'Chris, are you afraid of him?'

He laughed curtly. 'No, Liss, but I'm no fool. I know his reputation. I'm wary of him, that's all. When I'm ready ...' He broke off and she looked at him with anxiety.

'When you're ready, what? You aren't planning to play with him?'

'What did you find out about him?' Chris asked, evading her question. 'Did he tell you anything? Or just pump you dry and tell you nothing?'

She felt a curious reluctance to discuss Luc Ferrier with him. 'He didn't tell me anything,' she lied.

Chris made a little face. 'I didn't imagine he would have,' he shrugged. 'Why on earth did you talk to him in the first place? How did you come to run into him?'

She had never knowingly lied to Chris before. She had never hidden anything from him. Her nature and her old affection for him had made her as open as the day, but now she was evading issues, concealing feelings, and she felt alien to herself.

'I went for a walk in the forest and bumped into him,' she said.

Chris frowned. 'How did the subject of poker come up?'

'He noticed my ring,' she explained, not meeting his eyes. 'He asked me who I was engaged to and I told him. Then he told me he'd met you, played poker with you.'

'And what did you say?' Chris shot that back crisply, staring at her.

It took her a great deal to turn and meet his eyes without showing anything which was going on inside her. She was deeply aware of the deliberate nature of her smile at him.

'I told him I didn't approve of gambling.'

She saw Chris relax and he half-smiled. 'And what did he say to that?'

'He laughed,' Lissa shrugged, still keeping her eyes on him and smiling.

'So how did he come to offer you this bargain?' Chris demanded.

'He asked me to show him the sights of the town,' Lissa told him. 'And when I refused he suggested a bargain—if I took him round the town he wouldn't gamble with you tonight.'

His eyes narrowed. 'What happened while you were with him?' She saw his hands tighten at his side. 'He didn't touch you?'

Lissa could not stop the heat coming into her face and Chris watched it with a hardening stare.

'So he did! What did he do?'

'He kissed me,' she whispered, alarmed by the look in his face.

Chris grabbed her arms, staring down at her with a fixed, aggressive expression. 'And?'

Her eyes widened. 'And what?'

'And then?' he asked thickly, probing the wide

startled eyes. The fierce pressure of his fingers on her arms slackened and he gave a stifled sigh. 'That's all? One kiss and nothing else?'

'What do you think I am?' Lissa asked angrily. 'Do you think I wanted him to kiss me?'

Chris laughed shortly. 'So you didn't fancy him? Well, I didn't imagine you had, but you never know with women.' There was a cold twist to his mouth. 'Even girls like you can fall for a good line, and Ferrier certainly has a great line.'

Lissa frowned, disliking the cynical gleam in Chris's eyes. 'Well, I didn't.' She was lying and she knew it. She had not found Luc Ferrier's kisses distasteful. What's happening to me? she thought. She was meeting Chris's eyes and showing nothing of her secret thoughts, and her own ability to deceive was very disturbing.

'In future keep right out of his way,' Chris told her. 'If he tries it on again let me know and the boys will sort him out.'

Lissa shivered at the way Chris said that, the bright gleam of his eyes as he spoke.

As she walked back through to the foyer she met Rebecca. Lissa knew who had told Chris that she had gone off with Luc Ferrier. She met Rebecca's cold smile with an unsmiling stare of her own.

Pierre was in a teasing mood. 'I've had a request,' he told her. 'In fact, I've had dozens, for you to do the little song I wrote you. So how about it?'

Lissa flushed. 'I . . .'

'Come on, Liss,' he grunted. 'Either you want to be a professional or you don't. The people loved that song. They loved your dress, too. It's time you made up your mind whether you're going to give the people what they want or get out and let someone else do it.'

'Someone else meaning Jo-Jo,' she suggested, half smiling.

'Whatever,' Pierre said flatly. 'Chris wants you and you could be much better than you are, if only you'd do it the way the people want it.'

It wasn't the first time Pierre had said as much. She looked at him uncertainly. 'I feel shy when I sing it,' she muttered.

'Sure,' Pierre nodded, 'I know that. But you can sing it, Liss. All you have to do is grow up, for God's sake.' He put a thin arm round her shoulders in a brotherly hug, smiling. 'You were a sweet little kid, but now you're a woman. Start acting like one.'

There was so much she could say to that that the words all jammed up inside her head. She was frightened of changing, of becoming a full adult, and she knew it. She looked up into Pierre's round dark eyes and smiled pleadingly at him.

He gave her an encouraging nod. 'Going to try, baby?'

Lissa drew a deep breath and nodded. 'That's my girl!' Pierre grinned, hugging her again.

They went over the song a dozen times before he was satisfied with the way she was singing it. Lissa felt the provocative, ambiguous words sinking into her mind. They disturbed her even more now. Every time she sang them she thought about Luc Ferrier and her pulses raced. Pierre gave her an odd look when she was going.

'You're coming on,' he told her, grinning, and she wasn't sure what he meant by that, but knew she didn't want to know.

Chris gave her a sharp look as he saw her in the black dress that evening. 'I thought you preferred not to wear it,' he said with unhidden suspicion.

Pierre came up and winked at him. 'I talked her into it. The fans were demanding another look at it.'

Chris relaxed. 'Went down well, didn't it? I know. I got told as much over and over again.'

When Liss walked out into the spotlight her eyes involuntarily slid to the table where Luc usually sat and widened in surprise as she saw he was not alone. One of the other guests sat with him. Lissa had seen her several times before; she was one of the wives whose husband rarely left the gaming rooms. Luc was smiling into the woman's eyes and listening to whatever she was saying to him. The woman lifted her glass and sipped, fluttering her lashes at him over the edge of the glass.

She was a very attractive woman, Lissa recognised, suntanned, slim, her low red dress provocative.

Lissa felt a strange stab of anger and began to sing. She did not look at Luc again, but she sang as she had never sung before, using the purring voice she had heard Pierre use as he tried to get her to sing as he wanted.

It was nothing but mimicry. She remembered the teasing looks Pierre had given her as he sang certain lines and looked round the audience in the same way, smiling. She heard the laughter start, as it had started the first time she sang the song. She paused where Pierre had paused, smiled where he had smiled, and her slender body moved in the sinuous gestures Pierre had used as he sang.

She felt Pierre's excited look, saw his grin out of the

side of her eye. As she ended, the audience erupted in whistles and shouts, as they had before. 'More, more!' they yelled. Pierre bent forward and whispered: 'Sing it again.'

Lissa looked at him in startled disbelief. She had never sung a song twice before. Pierre nodded at her vigorously and struck up the bars which opened the song.

The audience clapped enthusiastically and Lissa, off balance, turned to launch into the song again. She felt a movement at the back of the room and saw Chris standing there. He had taken the red carnation from his buttonhole and held it in his fingers. He was shredding it absently, staring fixedly at her.

Something inside her hardened. She turned her eyes back to the grinning audience and began to sing.

The applause, the enthusiasm, had melted her inhibitions. She was relaxed, leaning on the piano, smiling. In the clinging black dress she suddenly had a new sophistication and was aware of it. Her old self was gone. She was no longer a little girl, Pierre had reminded her; she was a woman, and it was a woman singing, breathing out the witty lines, glancing past the smiling faces in the audience as though she invited an interest from them which in the past she would have run from like a terrified child.

She did not even look towards Luc's table. Walking off in a storm of applause, she found Chris waiting for her. His eyes had an odd harsh glitter in them.

Lissa looked at him defiantly, her mouth level.

Chris stared and didn't say anything, but his eyes were trying to read hers.

Lissa walked past him and went through the club to the foyer. She got Fortuné from the desk clerk and took him out into the warm still night.

She could not sleep after that. She felt wrung and yet elated, her mind confused with the rush of too many impressions. She watched the dog's white coat ahead of her and heard the sigh of the sea far off on the beach. The stars pierced the deep blue mantle of the sky, brighter than steel, sharper than knives. She stared up at them as she walked and shivered.

She would not think about the odd painful emotion she had felt before she began to sing.

She wouldn't think at all. She walked because her mind was far too wide awake for sleep and her body was restless and taut.

When she found herself on the edge of the pale beach she stood there watching the waves sigh up on to the sands. The dog ran down towards them, kicking up sand with his paws, printing the immaculate silvery beach with his marks.

The sound of movement behind her did not surprise her. She had known he was coming for at least a minute. She had been standing there, listening to his footsteps and shuddering like someone with a chill.

He came up behind her and stood there, breathing. Lissa stared at the sky, the sea, the silvery sands.

His hands touched her arms, slid caressingly down them, the cool brush of his fingers making her skin leap with awareness.

He moved closer, turning her to face him. She stood with lifted head and hard, wide eyes watching him as he watched her.

'Well, well, well,' he murmured. 'You are the most surprising creature, aren't you? What got into you tonight?'

She did not bother to reply. The peculiar anger inside her wouldn't let her speak.

His fingers ran down her cheek. He softly touched her folded lips with one of them gently tracing the warm moulded shape of her mouth. 'Why so silent?'

The tickling sensation of his finger went back and forward. He stared at her, brows sharply lifted.

'What's wrong, Lissa?' His tone had changed. The amused warmth had gone out of it and he was no longer smiling. 'What happened when you got back this afternoon? What did Brandon say to you?'

'Do you care?' She shot the words out like a dagger and saw his features tighten, his eyes narrow.

'What happened?'

'He told me never to see you again,' Lissa said icily. 'So please go back to the hotel, Mr Ferrier.'

His frown deepened. He took her slender shoulders in his hands and bent towards her, speaking curtly. 'Tell me! He was angry? What did he do? Did he threaten you?'

'Threaten me? Chris?' Her astonishment was in her face, but even as she threw back the words incredulously her mind was recalling the brutal violence in Chris's handsome face and she was shaken by the memory.

'He's no angel,' Luc Ferrier said harshly. 'His reputation on the island is far from pretty.'

Her eyes flew wide, her heart hurt inside her breast. 'What?'

Luc Ferrier's skin was taut, the hard bone structure

beneath it clenched. He looked as tough as Chris had claimed he was—he looked dangerous, ruthless, a man with eyes that bored into her own and made her deeply nervous.

'He runs this place with a private army, doesn't he? Those men in the gaming rooms would carve you up sooner than look at you. He has the island nicely organised. Makes money hand over fist, keeps a whole horde of women busy making the swag he sells in his shops, and pays them in peanuts to do it.'

'That's a lie,' Lissa said angrily, trembling.

'Is it? Do you know how much he pays them?'

'Do you?' she asked furiously, glaring up at him.

'Oh, yes,' he returned, taking her breath away. 'On average, I understand, he pays them one per cent of what he makes from the finished product.'

'One per cent?' Lissa's lips stiffened, dried. 'Who told you that? It's a lie!' It must be, she thought. Chris wouldn't, surely? Make money like that out of the local people? Cheat and manipulate them? Chris wasn't that sort of man. He was warm and friendly and kind. He wouldn't.

'It's the truth,' Luc Ferrier bit out, staring at her. 'Ask around. You know them all, you've known them all your life. Surely you must have realised how he ran this place?'

She ran her tongue tip over her dry lips and he watched the movement with an impassive face. 'Chris has to be firm with difficult customers. That's why he has so many men around the gaming rooms. Trouble can flare up if someone loses. Gamblers have volatile tempers.'

'That's what he told you?' Luc Ferrier said drily.

'Well, of course, it's true—up to a point. One or two tough boys are always around a place like this—but he has squads of them on tap. He doesn't just run the hotel, he runs the whole town. He's into everything from the tourist shops to the restaurants. He takes a percentage of that place we were eating at today.'

Her eyes wide and shocked, Lissa shook her head. 'No,' she muttered. 'I don't believe you.'

'Why should I lie?'

She looked at him fixedly and tried to decipher the hard strong face. 'You're making Chris sound like a gangster,' she protested.

Luc grinned humourlessly. 'He may use different words. He probably calls himself a businessman, but that's what he is, Lissa—a thug.'

'Don't!' she shivered, her brows drawn. 'Not Chris!'

He looked probingly into her anxious green eyes. 'Do you love him?'

'Of course I do,' she came back in a husky tone, but her eyes slid away from him. A week ago she would have been astonished by the question, given a firm and unthinking 'yes'. Now although she still made that positive reply she felt a strange tremor running through her, an uneasy flicker of uncertainty. Her love for Chris had been part of the backcloth of her life. She did not know what had changed. Herself, perhaps. She wasn't the same girl she had been a week ago. Odd things had happened to her, and all of them connected with this man.

She was half afraid Luc would press her, make her look at him. She knew instinctively that he was aware of the way her eyes had moved away as she spoke, but

he didn't say anything. He just watched the smooth
flushed oval of her face with a hard, intent observation
of which she was very conscious.

'You owe it to yourself to look at him very carefully
before you think of marrying him,' he said flatly.
'You're the type to whom marriage means a lifetime.
Before you sign up for life I'd take a good, hard look
at what you're getting, if I were you.' He paused, then
said slowly, 'Especially his women.'

The shock of that took her breath away. For a
moment she didn't move, then she looked up and asked
him in a voice which shook: 'Women?' He was lying;
he had to be. He wasn't talking about Chris, her Chris.
She had never seen Chris giving interest to any girl but
herself.

Luc stared down at her, his eyes glinting silver in the
moonlight which was streaming down the sky. 'You
didn't know about them, either?'

'You're lying,' she denied furiously, scarlet sweeping
up her face. 'Lying, lying! I don't believe you!'

'Jealous?' asked Luc in a harsh curt voice.

'I don't believe you. Why should I be jealous? Chris
wouldn't.' She glared at him. 'I've known him all my
life, practically. Do you think I wouldn't have noticed
if there was anyone but me around him?'

'He keeps the current woman on Joubeau Street,'
Luc said calmly.

She swallowed. 'Joubeau Street?'

'So I'm told. She's one of Pierre's cousins.'

Lissa swayed, feeling faint and sick. All the colour
went out of her face. She shook her head over and over
again, refusing to believe it, but she found it hard to
shut out the hard certainty of Luc's face. Her eyes clung

to him, pleading with him to say he was lying.

Luc slid his arms round her, supporting her. 'You'd better sit down,' he said curtly. 'You look as if you're going to pass out.'

She was too dazed to argue. She let him take off the white jacket he was wearing and spread it on the sand. He helped her to sit down on the jacket and sank down beside her. She was shivering as though she were icy cold, her head bent.

'Who told you all this?' she demanded.

'A little bird,' Luc drawled. 'An expensive little bird.'

'Expensive?' she stared, bewildered, then her breath caught in a long sigh. 'You paid someone? But they might have lied to you if you offered them money. You don't know these people. They're cheerful about making up stories to amuse visitors. They don't see it as telling lies, it's just a game to them.'

'This was no game,' Luc insisted. 'I got the truth.'

'You don't know Chris,' said Lissa, shaking her head.

'No, Lissa,' Luc denied, 'it's you who doesn't know him. The man you grew up with isn't the man you think he is.'

'People can't hide things like that, not for years,' she protested shakily.

'When someone like you is so damned innocent, they can,' Luc said with a grim smile. 'It wouldn't have entered your head to suspect any of this—to notice any of it. You've been drifting around with your eyes closed for the past couple of years and Brandon has seen to it that your eyes were kept shut as far as he could. All his people have strict orders to treat you with kid gloves.'

Lissa knew that. She wasn't so innocent that she hadn't been aware of the smiling, protective kindness surrounding her. Looking at Luc with disturbed anxiety, she asked: 'Is Chris in trouble? He isn't doing something illegal?'

Luc laughed brusquely. 'Hell, I doubt it. The law is as much in his pocket as everything else around here. He's got the place sewn up. His only danger is going to come when a bigger shark moves in and decides to take over from him. Once St Lerie is on the tourist map it will attract the attention of speculators elsewhere, then Brandon may have a fight on his hands. The kid gloves will come off then, Lissa. You'll see how tough he is if that happens.'

She stared down at the pale, moonlit sands. The dog was dancing through the waves excitedly, the faint splash of his movements coming clearly to her ears.

'What are you going to do?' Luc asked, his eyes on her averted profile.

She turned to look at him dully. 'I don't know.'

Luc drew in his lower lip. 'Don't face him with it, Lissa. It wouldn't be wise of you to do that. Just keep your eyes open from now on—stop seeing him in a romantic mist and start thinking. It doesn't take much digging to show what's going on underneath the tourist tinsel. All you have to do is use your eyes and your ears.' He paused, added, 'And your brain, Lissa. For God's sake, use that.'

'I wish you hadn't told me,' she broke out miserably.

Luc's brows twitched together in sharp anger. 'You would have preferred to stay in dreamy ignorance, would you? And married him? What then, Lissa? Are you prepared to share him with the lady in Joubeau Street? And turn a blind eye to his commercial activities?'

'I don't know,' Lissa groaned, confused and bewildered. 'No, of course not. But Chris ... I can't believe it.'

'You mean you don't want to,' Luc agreed. 'It would swallow you up too, Lissa. Don't you realise that? How long could you stay blind? And what would it do to you to find out later? You're changing already. That song you sang tonight—you sang it differently this time. You may not know it, but the scales are already falling and you may not like what he makes you. Corruption isn't always as simple as it sounds. It eats you up inch by inch like rust spreading on metal.'

'Chris loves me!' Her voice was low and he bent to hear her.

'Sure he does,' Luc said curtly. 'You're not only very sweet, you're potentially very sexy. You don't know it yourself yet. But he can see it and he's prepared to wait until you wake up. But he means to be the one to wake you. Brandon believes in monopolies. He's had you tied up and waiting for him for two years while he eases his frustration elsewhere. Lissa, open your eyes and look at him.'

She opened her eyes, but in the moonlight she was looking at Luc, her face pale and disturbed.

He lifted a hand to touch her cheek gently. She did not move, her green eyes enormous.

Luc kissed her softly, his lips moulding her own, brushing over them and returning.

Lissa drew back, breathing painfully. 'Don't,' she said under her breath.

Luc's hand dropped. He sat watching her.

'Why did you tell me all this?' she asked, staring at him.

His mouth twisted. 'Don't you think it was time someone did?'

'But why you? You paid someone to tell you these stories, you said.'

'I paid someone to dig up what they could about him,' Luc said. 'I hadn't expected to hear all that. I'd already realised he ran the casino like an armed camp. The rest of the stuff came as a surprise to me.'

'Why did you get someone to investigate Chris in the first place?'

Luc ran a hand through his black hair, grimacing. 'I was curious about him.'

'There's more to it than that,' she accused.

For a moment the blue eyes were as hard as steel, glittering between their shielding lids, then he shrugged. 'That's right, I told you, Brandon has something I want and I was trying to discover if he had any weak spots.'

Her body ran with a strange, cold flame. She looked away and Luc moved closer. She glanced back, shivering.

'Come away with me, Lissa,' he whispered. 'Let me take you out of all this—you can't marry Brandon.'

She was too confused to know what she felt or thought. She shook her head, feeling so brittle she would snap in two if he touched her.

'You're worse than he is,' she said bitterly. 'At least Chris loves me. Even if he's all the things you say he is—he still loves me. I may be stupid, but I'm not so stupid that I don't know what you want.'

'Do you?' He breathed close to her, his hard features unreadable. 'What do you think I want, Lissa?'

She turned her head sharply to look away. 'The answer is no, Mr Ferrier.'

'You don't even know the question,' he said mockingly.

She felt a peculiar melting sensation deep inside her as he moved even closer. 'Don't touch me,' she said shakily, jerking away and getting to her feet.

'I'm going to touch you,' Luc whispered, slowly raising himself from the sand. 'You want me to touch you.'

She shook her head fiercely. 'No!'

'Liar,' he breathed, smiling. 'From the minute I saw you on the beach that first morning I wanted to make love to you.'

'Is that why you told me all those lies about Chris?' she asked angrily.

'They were the truth,' said Luc. 'And so is this, Lissa ...'

She pushed at his chest as he drew her closer, his arms going round her. He laughed at her impotent attempts to escape the tightening circle in which he held her. 'Will you let go? I won't——' she began furiously, and was silenced by the driving force of a kiss that was unlike any kiss she had ever been given.

Luc's hands were behind her, pressing her against him, pinning her to the lean hardness of his own body, and his mouth plumbed hers, the warm moist invasion leaving her shaking. A groan escaped her and she tried to shut her mind to the insidious, coaxing movement of his hands as they stroked down her back and caressed her hips. Her hands dug into his chest, clenching. Her mouth opened weakly. She felt and heard the hoarse sigh Luc gave.

'Liss,' he muttered, his kiss flaring hungrily. His mouth crushed her lips, the demand he made so fierce that she swayed in his arms.

She had her eyes closed. All around them the palms breathed softly and the sea whispered on the moonlit sands. Luc's thighs were moulded to her body, forcing her to recognise the desire his mouth was reinforcing. Her hands slowly moved up to his shoulders, clung there, trembling against the warmth of his shirt.

Suddenly Luc lifted her off the ground and then lowered her again, but he had come with her and her eyes flew open in shock as she realised that she was lying full length on the sand with Luc's hard body pressing her down.

'Don't!' she groaned, pushing at his wide shoulders.

He looked at her with a twisted little smile. 'You're such an intoxicating mixture of innocence and fire, Lissa. You blush like a baby, but your eyes beckon. You don't even know what you're doing half the time, do you? It's all instinctive.'

She was too shaken by the wild tremors running through her body to be able to say a word, looking up at him and as much afraid of herself as of Luc.

'Come away with me,' he whispered. 'You can't stay here, and if you're honest you knew as well as I did the minute we met that this was going to happen.'

'No,' she muttered, stiffening under the powerful body which held her down with such ease.

'Don't lie to yourself,' he smiled. 'As soon as I set eyes on you I knew you were going to end up in my bed.'

Shock ran through her like fire. Her skin burned and her throat ached. She met the fierce flare of his blue eyes and shook her head dumbly.

'Your mouth promises so much more than you're prepared to admit,' he said huskily. He caressed her lips with his thumb, smiling at the helpless shiver which ran through her.

'Let go of me,' Lissa forced out through dry lips. 'You're not seducing me, Mr Ferrier, so get your hands off me!'

The smile vanished from his face. Slowly he lowered his head and she felt his lips on the underside of her chin, his breath warm on her flesh. 'Aren't I, Liss?' The deep, breathed question sent waves of panic along her nerves.

'No,' she whispered, trembling so hard it was painful.

He lifted his head and the blue eyes mocked her coolly. 'What a little liar you are,' he drawled. 'No? That isn't the truth, is it, Lissa? You make all the correct responses—trained to a hair by the good nuns, I've no doubt. But even while you're mouthing all that shocked stuff about my wicked liberty-taking, your eyes are begging me to go on.'

Lissa reacted like a scalded cat. She slapped him so hard her palm burnt and stung.

Luc's head rocked with the blow. The amusement went from his face and rage flashed down at her from his eyes. She felt instinctively that he almost hit her back, then his face tightened into an alarming mask.

'That was unwise of you, Lissa,' he drawled, his lips scarcely moving. 'You've made me angry now.'

She was quivering, watching him nervously.

He moved too fast for her to evade him. His dark head shut out the night sky. His mouth burned, bruised, delved into her own, forcing her to surrender her lips without a further protest. His hands moved possessively over her. Her dress was dragged down and his fingers slid down her shoulders to find the high, warm swell of her breasts.

Chris had never once touched her with such demanding intimacy. She had no previous experience of love-making to compare it with——whenever Chris had tried to accelerate their caresses anywhere near this point she had anxiously broken away from him. Now her own reactions were so fierce, so piercingly exciting, that she lost all sense of what she was doing, absorbed into a private dizzying world of pleasure.

The smooth, warm fingers held her trembling body and softly caressed it until she was groaning, yielding. Her heart beat so hard she was deaf. She couldn't think. She couldn't even hear her own voice as she gave those hoarse little sighs of pleasure. The roaring blood shut her ears and her eyes were blind as she twisted in Luc's exploring, arousing hands.

'Let me have you,' he whispered, and she heard the question through the singing of her blood and couldn't answer.

'You drive me crazy,' Luc muttered, his mouth at her throat, the demanding heat of it sliding down to the hollow between her breasts.

Lissa's hands dug into his back as his thigh forced itself between hers. Desire spiralled crazily inside her. A deep, heated urgency possessed her and her hands trembled as she touched Luc's body, her restless movements filled with driven necessity.

Luc suddenly sat up, breathing thickly. 'You see?' he asked in a low, unsteady voice. 'I could have you, couldn't I, Liss? Whatever you say, your reactions make that very clear.'

She felt horribly sick. She pushed him away, suddenly facing what had happened to her and reacting with shame and violence.

She scrambled to her feet, swaying weakly as her legs almost gave way under her. Luc stood too and held her elbow, his long fingers resting on it lightly.

'Stay away from me!' Lissa snapped. Humiliation and self-contempt were eating at her. The burning temptation of a moment ago had evaporated and she was sick.

'Come back to England with me,' Luc said quietly. 'You can trust me, Lissa. I'm no Brandon, I won't lie to you or cheat you.'

'I know what you want to do to me,' Lissa bit out.

'Oh, that,' he said, and laughed, and somehow it was the last straw. She looked at him savagely, then turned and walked away fast. Luc came after her, but as Lissa left the darkness of the palms fringing the beach they both heard voices. She halted and instinctively moved back into the trees. Luc came up with her and she looked at him nervously, her eyes wide.

'Brandon,' he said through his teeth.

'Looking for me,' she whispered. 'Luc, you must go. Don't let him see you.'

He studied her, his face calm.

'Please, please!' she whispered.

Luc bit down on his lower lip. 'I'm not leaving you,' he said.

'He won't hurt me,' Lissa muttered, flushing. 'But he might hurt you.'

Luc laughed harshly. 'You think I'm scared of him?'

'He has Max and several others with him,' she whispered. 'Max carries a knife, I'm sure he does.'

Fortuné had spotted the men and was running towards them, barking excitedly, pleased to see them.

'Go, please, Luc, do go!' she groaned, grasping his arm.

He hesitated then shrugged, and in a second he had melted into the darkness and she did not even see where he went.

She softly trod back through the palms and sat down where she and Luc had sat before. The impressions of their bodies lay there, betraying far too much of what had happened. Lissa quickly dragged a fallen palm leaf over the marks and began to draw a battlemented castle in the sand. Her hand shook, but she kept on drawing.

She heard the movements behind her and turned her head to look at Chris calmly, forcing every sign of guilt or fear out of her face. He stood there and behind him she heard the advance of his men.

For a moment Chris was totally silent. His narrowed hard eyes shot over her face, trying to read her expression.

He looked around. She had never noticed it before, but now she saw the raw violence which Chris held contained when she was around. His jaw was taut and his eyes flamed like hot metal.

The men stood, waiting, poised and dangerous. They were black shadows on the edge of the whispering palm, but the threat emanating from them was very real.

'What are you doing down here?' Chris asked softly. His eyes dropped to the sand around her, studied the disturbed surface.

'Drawing pictures,' she said, and she made her voice sound sulky and cold.

'Who's been here with you?' Chris asked, and she saw the flick of his eyes over the beach and realised with a shudder that the print of Luc's feet was only too visible.

'Mr Ferrier was down here,' she said, and felt Chris stiffen. He threw her a searching look.

'Oh?'

'He was talking to someone,' she said. 'They went off ten minutes ago.'

'Who was he talking to?' Chris demanded, and she knew he did not believe a word.

'I don't know her name. She was wearing a red dress.' Max moved and whispered in Chris's ear. Chris half turned his head and listened and the moonlight struck a medallion of his profile, turning it to the brutal harshness of a war leader. She had never seen cruelty and greed and violence in Chris before, but she saw them now.

He turned and looked back at her. She went on drawing her castle, making arrow slits in the walls, adding a flag on the top. Chris jerked his head silently and his men melted away.

He walked forward and stood there, his feet near her moving hand. Lissa did not look up.

'Why are you out here? What do you think you're doing?' he asked sharply.

Lissa had been searching her mind desperately for something to put him off the scent. She kept her eyes on her hand. In a low, angry voice she said: 'Why did you listen to Rebecca about me? Why do you encourage her to spy on me? Is she in love with you?'

Whatever Chris had been expecting her to say it had not been that, and the accusation took him by surprise.

'What?' he asked, shifting his feet.

She looked up, realising she had taken him off guard and pressing her advantage. 'Have you been flirting with her?' She stood up and glared at him. 'I hate you!' She used a furious, child's voice, letting it tremble, her lips quivering too.

'Honey,' Chris began, his body softening. 'Darling . . .'

She pushed him away as he tried to put his arm round her. 'Don't call me darling, tell me the truth. What have you been doing with Rebecca? She hates me—she showed it to me today. Why should she hate me?' Even as she made the accusation she was registering with surprise that it had already been in the back of her mind. Rebecca had looked at her with hostility. She often had in the past. Was she interested in Chris?

Chris was smiling. His voice was gentle and soothing. 'Baby, don't be silly.'

'I'm not silly!' Lissa retorted in the most childish voice she could manage. Her eyes stayed wide and bright, glazed with unshed tears. The tears were there already, tears of fear and disturbed realisation that she had never known Chris. But she used them ruthlessly, letting them slip from her trembling lashes. 'I'm not a baby, either. I didn't sing like a baby tonight. Pierre said I was very good. Don't patronise me any more. I won't be called a baby!'

Chris gave a little groan, half of laughter, half of passion. 'Darling Liss,' he said, looking at her with what she recognised now as a blatant, hungry desire for her. 'You certainly didn't sing like a baby. You turned me on so much I've got to have you, darling. Liss . . .'

She slapped his hands away. 'Don't touch me, you . . . you Lothario!' she shouted and ran.

Chris came after her, but she managed to reach the hotel first and bolted out of sight. She heard some guests halt him with eager, excited words. Chris hovered, trying to get away, and Lissa had time to get to her room. She locked the door and stood there, shaking.

'Liss,' he whispered a few moments later. 'Darling, let me in—I must talk to you. You're wrong—I've never laid a finger on Rebecca. She doesn't do a thing to me. God, Liss, don't you know I'm mad about you? Darling, open the door. Let me talk to you.'

'Go away!' she said in a high, cross voice.

'Liss!'

'Go away or I'll scream,' she promised.

Chris stood there. She could hear him breathing fast and hard. Waves of emotion came through the door and Lissa was frightened.

'You're frightening me,' she whispered unsteadily, and it was so true, the irony of it almost made her laugh.

Chris sighed. 'Okay, baby.'

'Don't call me that!'

'Oh, Liss,' he said wryly. 'Prove you're not. Open the door and let me love you.'

She didn't answer.

She heard other steps, a voice muttering. 'I've got to go, darling,' Chris said huskily. 'We'll talk tomorrow.

Tomorrow we'll fix our wedding day, Liss, and I won't take no for an answer.'

She heard him move away and slowly sank down on to a chair, her body huddled in fear and misery.

What was she going to do?

· CHAPTER FIVE

She did not sleep for hours. Luc's accusations about Chris went on sounding inside her head and she swung between angrily dismissing them and being forced to believe part of what he had said. She should have used her brain before. She should have looked more closely at the life around her. Now that she was looking she was finding disturbing hints of a truth she had bitterly ignored until now.

Chris had hidden too many things from her. She had seen the unveiled nature to which she had been blind for so long and, seeing him in that light, had felt the pattern of her vision shift into a new perspective.

Next morning, Luc was on the beach when she arrived. He turned and the first ray of sunlight struck across his broad, smooth shoulders and gave his skin a liquid, golden sheen that took her breath away.

'All right?' he asked tersely, moving to meet her, and she sensed anxiety in him.

She nodded, softened by the intent look of the blue eyes. 'Luc, I told Chris last night that you were on the beach with someone,' she said hurriedly.

'I know,' he nodded. 'I was listening.'

Lissa stared in disbelief. 'Listening? You didn't go?'

'I wasn't leaving you alone with him. I hung around in the palms and caught most of what was said.'

Lissa felt a pink colour creeping up her face. Luc had waited in the palm trees to make sure she was safe.

As soon as I was sure Brandon wouldn't harm you, I shot off to see Joanne,' he said.

'Joanne?' Lissa stiffened, her glance shooting to his face.

His eyes mocked. 'The lady in the red dress, remember?'

'Oh,' Lissa said coldly.

He grinned. 'I suspected Brandon would check on your story, and I was right.'

Lissa felt a shock of alarm. 'What?'

'The charming and murderous Max knocked on Joanne's door with a cock-and-bull story about a phone call for her husband. Lucas was in the gaming rooms. He rarely leaves them when they're open. Max knew that. Joanne viciously told him where he could find her husband and Max left.'

She should have suspected that Chris would go to some lengths to find out if she was telling the truth, but she wasn't yet accustomed to telling lies. She felt very sick. Chris wasn't the man she had thought she knew—all night she had been facing that and feeling like someone who has woken up to find themselves in a beautiful, but treacherous jungle. The air was heavy with sweet scents, but death lurked in every shadow.

Luc's veiled eyes were slipping down her slender body. The tiny white bikini seemed suddenly even more inadequate, and she had pulses beating at neck and wrist.

She thought of last night again and wondered what had happened between him and that woman. Lissa's feminine instincts did not need evidence to pick up the tingle of attraction which had been passing between them in the club last night. How long had Luc stayed in her room? And what had gone on?

She turned to walk down to the water and Luc followed, his feet sinking into the sharp gritty sand. They swam out into the blue water with the sun burning down on their heads. Halting to drift on her back, she heard the splash of his movement nearby and glanced sidelong at him. 'You ought to go back,' she said. 'I don't want Chris to see me with you.'

He nodded, accepting it. 'My yacht is ready to leave at a moment's notice,' he told her. 'The crew have been sleeping on board and going ashore by day. I can contact them down in the town and tell them to start off tonight.'

'When you leave is your business,' said Lissa.

Luc made a rough sound of impatience. 'You know what I'm saying. Will you come with me?'

She shook her head, the wet blonde hair plastered down the side of her face.

'Liss,' he said through his teeth, 'you can't stay here. You can't marry him.'

'It's my decision,' Lissa said flatly. 'Nothing to do with you.'

He stared at her, his face set. 'You don't fit into this set-up. If you stay you're going to regret it.'

A movement back on the beach drew their attention. Lissa flicked a look across the blue water and her whole body jerked with alarm. Chris stood there, in a tight-fitting blue T-shirt and skimp blue jeans, his slim body tense as he stared across the ocean at them.

'I told you to go away,' she moaned at him.

Turning, she swam back towards the beach and Luc followed. Lissa waded up out of the waves, feeling her limbs heavy with salt water and fear.

Chris did not move. He stood there, the hot steel of his eyes riveting her. Danger came out of him in waves.

Luc ran his hand through his stiff wet hair. His skin was gleaming with salt and his dark blue eyes were lazy, betraying none of the alarm making Lissa move so stiffly.

'Hallo, Brandon. Your fiancé swims like a fish,' he drawled. 'She tells me she disapproves of gambling. I hope that doesn't mean you're going to duck out on our arranged game.'

Lissa looked at him in sharp anger and disbelief. Although his tone was slow and cool he was challenging Chris directly.

She looked back at Chris, but he wasn't looking at her. He was staring at Luc with rigid features.

'Women and poker don't mix,' Luc murmured mockingly. 'Take my advice, Brandon, decide on one or the other. You can't run both. Women take you over and ruin you as a gambler.'

Chris still studied him as though trying to see right through his head. Lissa moved and Chris turned his head slowly to meet her eyes.

'You promised me,' she whispered, touching his bare brown arm. 'Chris, don't play poker with him.'

For another second Chris bored into her lifted green eyes, his face sharply angled. Then he smiled and she felt the tension seeping out of him. 'Run on back to the hotel, honey,' he said softly, patting her on the hip. His hand smoothed down her thigh intimately, possessively, and although she did not look at Luc she could feel his eyes on the little movement.

Lissa stared into Chris's eyes pleadingly. She was no longer afraid that Chris would lose heavily to Luc, yet she still feared that clash between them for a reason she could not quite put her finger on—her instincts warned her against the idea.

In the beginning Chris had wanted to beat Luc just because Luc was a famous player; now she knew without needing to be told that Chris had other reasons for wanting to beat Luc. She was terrified of what might happen if, as she strongly suspected, Luc beat Chris hands down.

Chris smiled tightly at her. 'Run along, honey,' he said in a voice which left her no option.

She went slowly, feeling sick. The vivid sunlight, the gaudy flesh of the tropical flowers, seemed hateful to her for the first time. She had once loved this place. Now she felt she could not bear the sight of it.

Why had Luc done it? Why had he deliberately dared Chris to a duel? He must know the dangers he ran. Lissa did not investigate too closely on what her own suspicions were based, but she knew Luc would be in danger if he won against Chris.

There was to be a dinner-dance that evening in the club and Lissa was due to sing for the guests. She rehearsed with Pierre for a while and then went down into the town. She wandered through the gay shopping centre without really noticing much. At a distance she saw Joanne Lucas in a flower-printed sun-dress which left her slim thighs bare. The woman was smiling to herself with a sensuality which made Lissa's teeth meet. The absent, amused expression on Joanne Lucas's face sickened her.

Had Luc stayed in her room long? Had he gone to bed with the woman? What did she know about him, anyway? She had only met him a few days ago and she only knew about him what he had told her himself. She had known Chris all her life and loved him more than anyone she had ever met. Her mother had been a distant memory, her father always drinking. Chris had been brother, friend, lover to her. Why should she blindly accept what a stranger told her about him?

She went into the fort and wandered around there in the bat-haunted crumbling walls listening to the roar of the surf and the laughter and cries of swimmers and surfers.

In a few short days everything in her world had changed, including herself. She felt as though she had been half alive, a formless creature, half child half woman, but now Luc had somehow brought her fully to life, stiffened her dreamy contentment into something very different.

She felt fully mature for the first time in her life. Her mind was thinking harshly, certainly, and she was suffering the ravages which maturity can bring.

Now that Luc had opened her mind to it there were so many little things she had noticed but never thought about. The whole luxurious, soft-centred ambiance of the hotel, the island, had been part of her life for so long that it had never occurred to her to question any of it. She had heard snatches of talk, seen Chris and his men move in on someone who was causing trouble, without thinking about it. She had blithely accepted Chris's standards, his ready explanations.

If Luc was right, she could not marry Chris. She could not live this sort of life.

Joubeau Street lay at the back of the town. Lissa knew the place. She thought of Chris going there, spending time with some woman, and was forced to recognise that although the idea appalled her she was not jealous. She had felt a sharp stab of jealousy as she saw Luc smiling at Joanne Lucas, but she had only felt horror and disbelief when she was told that Chris had a mistress.

The realisation that Chris had been lying to her, deceiving her, was what horrified her. It revealed an abyss between them. She did not know Chris; she never had. It was not merely that their whole relationship was false. The premise on which her life had been based was false, too. This whole island was riddled with corruption. Under the sleek gaudy beauty lay a poisoned root reaching down into darkness.

It was only as she walked back to the hotel that the realisation dawned on her.

How was she going to get away?

Chris was not going to let her leave the island; Lissa could be sure of that. He would keep her there by hook or by crook and he would make her marry him. He had disguised from her his nature for so long, but now she could see through the lazy goodhumoured charm to the avid cruelty beneath it.

Chris wanted her. Her blood ran cold at that idea. She remembered the hot metal of his eyes as he reached for her last night, the hoarse sensuality of his voice.

He had been waiting for two years and he wasn't going to be cheated of his prize now. If he had genuinely loved her she might have appealed to that love, but she saw now that it was physical hunger that governed Chris. He lusted for her. Her face burned, she felt sick. It was a vile word and she had never thought she would apply it to Chris, but it was the only one that covered the truth. Lust lay in his eyes, in his voice. She should have seen it before, but she hadn't.

Watching him last night as she sang, shredding a red carnation jerkily between his fingers, she had been watching a man convulsed with lust, and she hadn't even known it until now. She had felt something ugly and frightening inside him, but she hadn't known what it was she felt until now.

Chris found the wide-eyed innocence she had always had deeply attractive, but for the worst of reasons. He ached for the day when he would destroy it. He had deliberately held her in it, waiting for his moment, and he would not forgo that pleasure now. He intended to have her.

When she went into the hotel she found Max and Uncle Joey talking to the desk clerk. She smiled cheerfully at them all, her eyes wide and bright. 'Hallo. Where's Chris? I bought a new bikini and I want to show it to him.'

Max gave her a sly sideways smile. 'Gone across the island to see someone,' he said, and Lissa shrugged, pouting.

As she reached her own room her face could relax from that sweet, childlike, artificial smile.

She was appalled by her own ability to lie, to pretend. She was sickened by the necessity, but she had to make them all think she was still the same. She had to maintain that little girl manner, smile as warmly, talk in the same light happy fashion.

Chris must not see, must not guess, the changes which had taken place in her. The moment he did he would move in to the kill.

Sitting down on her bed, she wondered why he had never made a serious attempt before. Looking back over the past two years she could see that Chris had been impatient for his final possession of her, but he had never gone beyond the line her own innocence had drawn between them.

Why?

Did he care more for her than mere lust? Or had he known that if once she saw through his charming mask she would run away? Had he been hoping that she would be too deeply in love with him to care any more? Had he been waiting because he sensed she was not yet physically awake?

Over the past couple of days she had felt the constant search of his eyes. He sensed a change in her, although he wasn't sure about it yet. If he once guessed that overnight she had become physically, mentally, emotionally, a woman, he would rush to claim her.

She looked into the mirror, face quite white now. She could not bear the idea of lying in Chris's arms any more.

She sheered away from any admission as to her reasons for such revulsion. It wasn't Chris who had pulled her across the line dividing child from woman, but Lissa refused to let herself dwell on that fact.

The rush of experience, feeling, was confusing her, but under it her mind was working with hard clarity. She had never known just how clearly she could think.

Her first reaction to Luc's unveiling of the sort of world she lived in had been one of distress and anxiety. She had felt a loyalty to Chris which the shock of the truth had battered but left intact. Today that loyalty had crumbled, and she wasn't sure why. She had been thinking all day and as her mind sifted through the various elements of the problem she had slowly come to realise that Chris and the island no longer meant anything to her.

She had always seen herself as Chris saw her. She had fluttered around him like a tropical butterfly whose wings he did not want to damage even though he longed to capture it and hold it between his hands.

Now she knew the image, the picture, had been false. She was not like that. Reality was far distant from the gaudy, fragile dream.

Her own reflection in the mirror showed her a slender girl with clear, hard green eyes and a firm mouth. Her years at the convent had given her a backbone of principle. Chris had never been able to dispel the influence of the nuns, however hard he mocked them. Other girls at the school had giggled over their moral teachings, but Lissa had been more open to it. She had accepted it without thinking and she knew it held good now.

The attitudes of the hotel, the way of life Chris followed, would never have suited her. She had been protected from the full blast of them. Chris had protected her for his own reasons, but he had, all the same, protected her, sheltered her from the slow stain of his world.

She was going to have to walk away from him, from the island. She considered Luc's offer to take her with him and her skin grew taut. She did not need to guess what sort of price Luc would set on his help. He might not approve of Chris, but his own attitudes were hardly admirable. Luc wanted her too. Chris wasn't the only one whose eyes held heat and urgent desire when they looked at her.

Lissa put her hands over her eyes, shuddering. She had never felt the drag of Chris's physical nearness, but every time Luc Ferrier was anywhere near her, her body shivered with reaction.

She wasn't walking out of the frying pan into the fire. She would have to make her own way somehow. But how? She had little money. Chris had always been very generous to her, but his generosity took the shape of presents: clothes, jewellery, ornaments. He paid her a salary, but Lissa had never saved much of it. She had not realised until now just how financially dependent she was—now she saw that Chris had her more securely than she had realised.

Her act was timed to take place half-way through the dance that evening. She ate with Chris and felt the constant glitter of his eyes as he watched her. She was wearing the black dress, at the request of the guests again. Pierre had teased her about it. 'They really fancy you in it, Liss,' he had said, and she had not had to pretend to blush.

She blushed now as she caught Chris's eye and he leaned over to whisper to her. 'Fix that date.' He was teasing, smiling, but his eyes did not hold any smile at all; they were filled with a liquid heat that dismayed her.

The pressing menace of his desire left slivers of ice in her veins. 'I'll need a trousseau,' she parried lightly, smiling at him, and marvelling at her own new-found ability to act.

'Name it,' Chris breathed, stroking her arm with

trembling fingers. 'Buy what you like tomorrow.'

'Tomorrow?' She laughed, shaking her head. 'I'll need more than one day.'

'Do you know what I need?' Chris was losing the ability to control the heat inside him and she could see it. 'Baby, it's got to be soon. Stop playing around.'

'Next month?' she suggested. It seemed a long time ahead now and by the time it came closer surely she would have thought of a way out?

'Next month,' Chris said hoarsely, nodding. He bent his fair head over her arm, kissing it moistly. 'Liss, Liss,' he groaned.

When the dancing began Lissa gave him a light, flirtatious little smile. 'Aren't you going to dance with me?'

He had been talking in a low voice to Max, out of her hearing, but he came over to smile and take her hand to lead her out on to the floor. Max and the other two men with him watched, grinning broadly.

Held close to Chris, both his arms round her, his hands on her slender shoulderbones, she felt the pressure of his tense thighs on her body and had to resist the shiver running through her.

She leaned her cheek against his face and his arms tightened. 'God, I want you, Liss,' he muttered, nibbling her ear.

Over his shoulder her eyes met those of Luc Ferrier. He was dancing with Joanne Lucas. The woman was moving sensually against his lean body, both arms round his neck. Luc's face was hard and unreadable as Lissa looked at him.

She looked away, a very faint warmth creeping into her cheeks. Chris was kissing her neck now and she felt the excitement inside him with wary alarm.

She wriggled. 'Don't,' she whispered. 'People are watching.'

He grinned and drew back a little. 'What a little rabbit you are,' he teased. 'Does it matter? Do you think I care what other people think?'

'I don't like being stared at,' she muttered.

'You'll have to get used to it,' Chris told her with a twist of the lips. 'With a body like yours you're going to be stared at whatever you do.'

She could not control the burning blush rising in her face and Chris watched the colour with half-impatient amusement.

'You've got the sexiest body I've ever seen,' he murmured into her ear, his breathing quickening again. 'Didn't you know that? When you move every man in sight goes crazy and that wide-eyed stare of yours makes you all the more exciting.' He laughed thickly. 'God, Liss, when you do wake up you're going to be something. You're going to be as sexy as hell one day.' She felt his hand sliding up and down her body, his fingers gripping her, and over his shoulder she met Luc's narrowed, flintlike eyes and could not hold them.

Max came over to tap Chris on the shoulder and whisper. Chris turned his head, listening, made a wry face. 'Okay, I'm coming.' He released Lissa and gave her a quick smile. 'Sorry, angel. I'll be back in ten minutes. Don't go away.'

He left her at their table and vanished with his men treading behind him like dogs on his heels. Lissa stared after them all and her face was cold and hard. Oh, she saw it now. She must have been blind not to see it long ago. Chris hid his nature under his charm, but she should have seen the real man in the way all those toughs from the back alleys of Ville-Royale took his orders, leapt to the soft sound of his voice, prowled at his heels.

A figure moved on the periphery of her vision. She turned and Luc leaned there casually, watching her, his features tight and cold.

'Enjoying the evening?' he asked. 'You and Brandon dance well together. 'I'm sure there are going to be other things you do well together very soon.'

The deliberate, slashing insult made her stiffen and glare at him. Luc ran his icy eyes down her body. 'I don't blame him. In that dress you're a walking invitation. You've decided to stick with the devil you know, have you?'

'I haven't decided anything,' Lissa threw back fiercely. 'It's none of your business—but then that wouldn't bother you, would it? You think you've got some God-given right to interfere and criticise and do as you please!'

His dark blue eyes held a spark of angry amusement. 'Stop spitting like a ruffled cat and dance with me,' he said, taking hold of her wrist and jerking her to her feet as though she were a child.

'No,' she refused, shaking her head.

She said it again as Luc drew her into the intimate crowd of other dancers. 'I don't want to dance,' she hissed, and he took her wrists and placed her arms round his neck.

His own arms went round her and drew her so close she felt the lithe hardness of his body against her own and a slow shiver of pleasure ran through her. Luc looked down into her eyes and Lissa knew he had felt her physical reflex reaction.

'Why did you challenge Chris?' she flung angrily. 'Are you mad?'

'No,' he drawled. 'Very sane, in fact. It distracted him.'

'Can't you see how dangerous it would be?'

'I can take him,' said Luc, and she remembered Chris saying that and her green eyes were as fierce as a cat's, angry and frightened and anxious.

'Don't!'

'Don't take him?' Luc raised his dark brows in sardonic query.

'Don't say that,' she muttered. 'That's what Chris says. I hate those words.' She looked at him bitterly. 'And he thinks he can beat you too.'

'Of course he does,' Luc shrugged indifferently, his face casual and uncertain. 'But he can't.'

'How can you know that?' she flared in anger.

He smiled at her, his lips crooked. 'Sweetheart, you can be sure of that. I know. Brandon couldn't win against me even if he had the devil's own luck.' His eyes mocked her. 'And he hasn't got that, has he? I have. Don't you know what they say about me? The devil gives me the cards, and I know how to play them.'

'It isn't funny,' Lissa said huskily. 'Don't talk like that.' Lucifer, she thought, watching the saturnine harshness of his face as he stared unsmilingly at her. Yes, it was a very apt nickname. The winged darkness of his brows, the stark bones beneath the smooth brown flesh, the tight cold mouth as he watched her, all gave the nickname the ring of absolute truth.

Luc looked dangerous when he did not smile. He looked tough and icy and immovable.

'You're a funny sort of stockbroker,' she said with anger and pain.

He laughed under his breath, his face altering. 'I learnt it at my father's knee,' he told her.

'Was he a stockbroker?'

Luc's eyes danced. 'Not quite. He dealt in stocks and shares, all right, but I don't think you could call him a stockbroker. You couldn't call me one, either. Not strictly speaking.'

'You said . . .'

'You misunderstood me,' Luc drawled. 'I said in passing that I dealt in the stock market in London. I buy and sell shares. It's all a question of knowing when to do it.'

'You don't have an English name,' she realised.

'That's because I'm not English,' he agreed. 'French by descent, anyway. I was born in England, actually, but my father was born and brought up in Paris.'

'If you're not a stockbroker, what are you?'

He threw her a dry glance. 'A rose by any other name,' he said, and she felt a surge of rage at the evasive nature of the answer.

'Don't tell me if you don't want to,' she snapped.

'I never do anything I don't want to,' he agreed softly.

'I don't believe you've got a job at all!'

He laughed shortly. 'Don't you?'

'You were just filling my head with fairy stories.'

'Don't confuse me with Brandon,' Luc drawled.

'I won't,' she said with a raging huskiness that made him stare at her intently.

She looked away because the sudden sharpness in his

eyes disturbed her. Her anger and deep sense of attraction had made her voice far too betraying.

Staring over his wide shoulder, she kept her eyes on the band and saw Pierre watching them. As Luc slid her smoothly across the floor she felt the back of her neck prickle with the feeling of being watched. But it was not Pierre's eyes that were sending that quiver of disturbance through her. It was Chris whose stare was making her feel nervous and uptight.

The music came swirling to a stop. She suspected Pierre had got a nod from Chris to halt. Luc's arms dropped from her and they moved off the floor.

Chris stood there, elegant and very tense in a white evening jacket. His bright, hard eyes met those of Luc Ferrier. 'Mine, I think,' he said as he took her hand, and the tone, the words, meant far more than the smile he gave Luc pretended.

Luc smiled. His facial muscles moved, his lips twisted. To a casual eye it could be called a smile, but the icy glint of his eyes made it clear it was nothing of the sort.

'When are you and I going to fight it out?' he asked with a reckless excitement in his voice.

Chris glanced at Lissa briefly. 'Liss doesn't approve of gambling,' he said.

She began nervously to speak and Luc cut her dead before a word had fully escaped.

'That's tough,' he said viciously. 'I never let women get in my way, but if you're that sort of man maybe it would be as well to forget it, anyway.' He turned on his heel with a contemptuous smile and Lissa heard Chris take a deep, angry breath. His face had reddened. His eyes were murderous.

'Tonight,' he said to Luc's back, hurling the word at him like a knife.

Luc halted. He turned his black head and smiled. 'Tonight, then,' he said before he moved away.

Lissa was shaking with terror and shock. She clutched at Chris's sleeve. 'No! Don't, Chris—you promised!'

'I don't take that sort of slap around the face from anybody,' he said furiously. 'You heard what he said. You got the implication as well as I did. Nobody calls me a coward and gets away with it.'

'You promised,' she whispered.

'I know,' he muttered, his face still a dark red. 'But I can't keep my promise. After tonight I swear to you . . .'

'If you play with him I won't marry you,' Lissa said on a desperate note.

Chris looked at her with a narrowed surveillance. He smiled at her. 'Oh, yes, you will,' he said, and then he walked away.

CHAPTER SIX

Lissa barely knew what she was doing as she went into her act. The music beat inside her head and her lips opened and shut, emitting sounds, but she might as well have been alone on a desert island. The applause, the watching eyes, did not impinge upon her consciousness.

Fear streaked along her nerves. Chris had looked vicious as he stared after Luc. When he told her that she *would* marry him he had had cold determination in his eyes.

Once she had seen weakness in him, a flaw running through his charming façade, but now she had been brought to recognise that he was weak in quite a different sense from the one she had imagined. His weakness lay in a sort of strength Lissa had never known him to display. He was coldly, cruelly determined on his own way. It was still weakness—but he had shored himself up with his murderous gang of henchmen, his power over the lives of everyone on the island. It was power which gave his weakness the icy glitter of danger. Chris had no moral scruples to make him halt in anything he did, in the pursuit of anything he wanted.

She left the club and collected Fortuné from the desk clerk. The dog shot off into the night and Lissa followed slowly, biting her lip. How could she sleep tonight? She couldn't calmly go to bed while Luc was facing Chris across a table and fighting a duel whose outcome could be disastrous whichever way it went.

She lingered to inhale the scent of honeysuckle, the creamy yellow flowers thickly clustered on their bushes. While she stood there in the shadows of the garden she heard a step and shivered, looking round.

Luc halted to stare at her. His face was unreadable, but she could sense hostility.

'Don't play with him,' she begged, pulling one of the flowers down. The petals showered on the grass at her feet and she twisted the stem restlessly, her eyes on Luc's dark features.

'It's fixed for midnight,' he said coolly. He moved closer and she saw the sudden flare of his eyes, their brightness lighting up his face. 'Lissa, it's a perfect opportunity for you to get away. The whole place will be in the gaming rooms. All his men will be there. Nobody will see you leave the hotel. Pack a few things and slip out around one in the morning.'

'Where could I go?' she asked wildly. 'Where do you think I could hide on this island?'

'I've fixed that,' Luc said.

She stared at him, her eyes enormous.

'Go down to the beach where we usually swim. One of my men will be waiting for you. He's going to bring a dinghy and row you out to the yacht. You'll be safe out there during the night.'

For a moment Lissa felt a sick relief, then she looked hard at him. Luc would be staying to play that game with Chris. He would be hostage for her. Once Chris discovered she had vanished he would immediately suspect Luc, and her heart winced at the thought of what Chris might do to Luc.

'I can't,' she whispered.

Luc's body clenched. She saw his mouth tighten, his

eyes glitter. 'You stupid little fool, you can't still hanker after him! The man's a barracuda. His teeth are stripping every ounce of flesh off this island and he's hungry to strip you, too. Get away from him while you can.'

'You don't understand——' she began, and he broke in with a muttered curse.

'Damn you to hell, Lissa, have some sense! You're blind about him. Can't you see ...'

'Luc——' she interrupted huskily, putting a hand on his sleeve.

He caught her shoulders painfully, flinging her head back, and his mouth burnt fiercely, angrily, on hers. She felt the violent movements of it like blows. Luc was kissing her with rage, his lips forcing hers until she felt the tender skin inside her mouth grinding against her teeth.

She struggled wildly. He was hurting her and she felt his anger so deeply she wanted to cry.

'Stay with him, then,' Luc bit out, releasing her.

Lissa felt his hands fling her away and stumbled, clutching at the honeysuckle bush. Luc walked away into the darkness and the tears began to run down her face.

She could not go back to the hotel in that state. She walked around the garden in the shadows and once or twice saw silent-footed shadows patrolling the grounds. Chris's men prowling around—in search of her? she wondered. She froze into the darkness and waited until they had gone. Fortuné came softly up to push his nose into her hand and she knelt to hug him.

As she walked back to the hotel she walked into Rebecca and got a quick, hostile glance from the other girl. Rebecca's eyes narrowed on the tearstains visible on Lissa's cheeks. 'Had a row with Chris?' she asked in a wry voice.

'You'd love that, wouldn't you?' Lissa flung back. 'Does he know you're in love with him?'

Rebecca's colour ran angrily. 'I'm not!'

'No?' Lissa stared at her. Rebecca knew everything that went on at the hotel. Chris might have hidden the sort of operation he was running from her, but he wouldn't have hidden much from Rebecca. How could he? Rebecca was always around his office. Carefully Lissa said: 'He must find it very useful to have a doting secretary. You'd die rather than give away a thing about what goes on here, wouldn't you, Rebecca?'

The other girl's brows flicked together. She stared at Lissa sharply. 'What are you talking about?'

Lissa didn't answer. She just smiled, her eyes mocking.

'You're not the wide-eyed innocent he thinks you are, are you?' Rebecca broke out with shrill dislike. 'I've seen the way you look at that Ferrier man and the way he looks at you. You've been pulling the wool over Chris's eyes long enough. The only reason he was going to marry you was because he didn't think he'd get you any other way, but he's wrong, isn't he? He probably got beaten to you a long time ago. I bet Ferrier wasn't even the first. Chris has been a fool about you.'

'Chris loves me,' Lissa said very softly, watching her.

'He said he loved me once,' Rebecca muttered. 'I should have been as bright as you are—waited for a wedding ring before I lost my head. It was too late when I realised just what sort of man he really was. I'll hand it to you—you're clever. I didn't think anyone could make a fool of Chris, but you've done it. Just don't imagine you can go on doing it. Once he realises he isn't the first he'll kill you. He won't like it when he discovers he's been had.'

Lissa shivered and Rebecca watched her with a fierce smile. 'I wouldn't like to hazard a guess what he'll do to you. Girls who run foul of him come to no good.'

'What about the girl on Joubeau Street?' Lissa asked casually, hoping Rebecca could not see the shock and horror inside her.

It surprised Rebecca. She saw the startled expression come into the other girl's eyes. 'You know about her? He didn't tell you.' Rebecca laughed curtly. 'Pierre, was it? Chris will cut his throat!'

'No, not Pierre,' said Lissa. So it was true, she thought. It was all true. And tonight Luc was facing him across the table, risking not only money in their encounter. The darkness inside Chris made him unpredictable and dangerous.

Rebecca was staring at her, biting her lip. 'Are you going to tell him what I've said?'

Giving her a wry look, Lissa shook her head.

'It cuts both ways, remember,' Rebecca warned. 'I've got a few things I could tell him about you.'

'You keep your secrets, I'll keep mine,' said Lissa, turning to go.

Rebecca caught her arm, her long talons of nails digging into her flesh. 'Look, if you've got any sense you'll get the first plane out of here. Chris can be vicious.' She glanced around nervously. 'I wish to God I'd never got involved with him.' Releasing Lissa, she hurriedly vanished and Lissa went slowly into the hotel.

She could not go quietly to bed. She had to know what was going on between Chris and Luc. She left

Fortuné in her room, washed and did her make-up again, then went down to the gaming rooms.

The men on the door looked at her in surprise but let her pass without question. One of them had an amused expression and she guessed he thought she had come because she was worried about Chris. Everyone knew she did not approve of his playing poker.

She walked through the spacious, luxurious public rooms, where faces bent avidly around the roulette table, the chandeliers casting a harsh cruel light over them. One of the croupiers watched her, smiling, and Lissa smiled back brightly.

Max was on the door behind which Luc and Chris were playing. He stood with folded arms, watching her walk towards him, his narrowed eyes skimming the half-revealed curves of her body in the black dress.

Lissa managed to look calm and unconcerned, but she was very aware of the way his eyes slid over her. She had never much liked the atmosphere in these rooms, but now she loathed them. She knew it would kill her to stay here on the island in this place. She had to get away before the poison leaked into her own veins.

He did not move to let her pass and when his eyes came up, Lissa met them with raised eyebrows and a light smile.

'Can't I go in?'

'Chris said nobody was to go in,' Max told her.

Lissa lowered her lids. She thought quickly, coldly. Putting a hand up to Max's bow tie, she pulled it loose with a teasing little smile. 'That doesn't include me, does it? I'm not nobody.'

Max's eyes flickered at the deliberate flirtation. She had never thought about it before, but now she guessed

Max found her attractive. His eyes told her as much as he looked down at her.

'I'll ask him,' he compromised, turning.

He opened the door and she slipped through with him. Max turned his head to frown and Lissa gave him an impudent little grin.

'I can ask him myself,' she mocked.

She walked towards the table in the centre of the room. The rustle of her black dress caught Chris's ear and he turned his head to stare at her with hard, watchful eyes.

Max hovered, waiting for his orders.

Luc surveyed her icily as she walked round to Chris. Ignoring him, she put a hand on Chris's neck, her fingertips stroking the short fair hair bristling on the nape. She felt the shudder run through him.

'So you are playing,' she said with a faintly sulky look, bending to meet Chris's eyes.

Chris put down his cards and leaned back in his chair to smile at her. His eyes held a mixture of amusement, relief and physical desire as they ran over her.

'Checking up on me? I'm beginning to feel married.'

'No, you're not,' said Lissa, flickering a look at him through her lashes.

She saw the flash of excitement in his eyes. She had never looked at him teasingly, provocatively, before, and Chris loved it. He took her hand and began to kiss her arm lightly, his mouth lingering on her wrist, the smooth cool inside skin, her inner elbow.

'You can't stay. I can't concentrate on the game with you here.'

'Can't you?' She smiled down into his eyes.

Little beads of perspiration came out on his forehead

and upper lip. 'Liss,' he muttered, his other hand curving round her head and pulling her down to kiss him. She submitted without protest, letting her lips part under the moist invasion. Chris ran his hand down the warm curve of her body and she heard the muffled gasp of his pleasure.

Then he slapped her lightly, drawing back. 'I'll see you later, sweetheart,' he said huskily. 'Off you go for now.'

Luc was staring down at the table, his face and body rigid. Lissa put her finger to her lips and laid it on Chris's cheek, then she turned and walked across the room past Max.

As she went out she turned and saw Chris watching her. The avid probe of his eyes sickened her, but she smiled at him over her shoulder before she went.

She had done what she could, she thought, going up to her own room. She had had to put Chris off the scent, put him into a relaxed frame of mind which might help Luc. Her provocative behaviour, the kiss she had given him, had partly distracted Chris from his game, and Lissa knew it. He would now have an undivided mind as he played his cards. She had put her own image into Chris's head, promising a pleasure which would constantly come between him and what he was doing.

She hurriedly took off her black dress and dressed in a black sweater and jeans. They wouldn't be seen easily at night and they would be warm when she was on the boat.

She packed a few necessary items in a light bag, gathered up Fortuné under her arm, whispering to him not to make a sound, and then she carefully locked her door. Chris might come up later to try it. She had a shrewd idea he would. She had been inviting him with every look she gave him and Chris was not going to be slow in taking her up on it. She hoped the idea was eating into his brain even now. She hoped he was hardly aware of the cards he was getting.

Her room looked out on to the garden. As a child she had often climbed down the gnarled, deformed branches of the sycamore which grew close to the wall. She hadn't tested the strength of it lately. She would have to trust to luck that she could make it bear her weight.

Opening her window, she quietly slid out and looked down into the darkness. There wasn't a sound, a movement. She dropped her bag and watched it fall into a flowerbed. Listening, she waited, and when there was still no sound she slithered down into the first wide fork. It was difficult with the dog clutched in her arm. He wriggled nervously, whimpering, and she put her hand over his muzzle. 'Ssh!' she begged.

She was almost at the base of the tree when she heard movements. Freezing against the trunk, she held her breath and kept a hand over the dog's jaws.

A figure walked slowly past. She recognised one of the men from the gaming rooms. His eyes swept around the gardens in watchful intensity, and Lissa trembled.

He seemed to take hours to get out of sight as he patrolled round the other side of the hotel.

When his steps died away she jumped the last of the way to the ground and grabbed up her bag from among the clustered flowers. Still carrying the dog under her arm, she began to run from tree to tree, slipping and sliding on the grass.

It was only as she began to make her way through

the palm trees along the edge of the beach that it occurred to her that Luc's man might have come and gone, or not arrived at all.

Heart racing, she stood in the trees, searching the sands. There wasn't a sound, a sight, of anyone.

Lissa felt sick. She swallowed and gazed across the rolling waves. Luc's yacht was anchored around the bay off Ville-Royale. She stared in that direction, but there wasn't a sign of any craft heading towards the hotel beach.

Luc's man had not come. She walked out of the trees, her eyes glinting with unshed tears, and moved slowly down the beach. All that trouble for nothing. How was she to get back into her room? She would have to climb up the tree again with Fortuné under her arm and it wouldn't be easy.

The sound was so tiny she thought at first she hadn't heard it, then another came and she whirled round, gasping with alarm and fear.

The shape moved warily, coming closer.

'Miss?' The whispered question was a mere breath. 'Come over here.'

Lissa peered through the darkness, not moving.

'You waiting for a boat?' the man asked, still not coming any closer. 'You're in the moonlight over there, you'll be seen. We must start off down the far end. Walk down there slowly.'

Lissa swallowed and began to walk. She heard the other movements and at last she was in the shadow of the tree-hung cliff at the far end of the beach.

She heard the splash with which the dinghy was launched. 'Hop in,' the man muttered.

Fortuné did not like the look of the boat and the man

did not like the look of the dog. 'He coming?' he asked
with dismay.

'I can't leave him,' Lissa whispered. 'I can't.'

He shrugged and sighed. She settled down, the cold
rubber of the dinghy against her arm, and the boat shot
away from the shoreline.

'What is Mr Ferrier going to do?' she asked the man,
peering at him. 'How will he get away?'

He grinned, showing white teeth. 'Luc will manage.'

The casual confidence did not soothe her. She twisted
her fingers in her lap, biting her lip.

'What if there's trouble?'

'Trouble is Luc's middle name,' the man replied
easily, laughing under his breath. 'And he's been in
tighter spots than this—you should have been with him
in Rio when he was jumped by two guys with knives. I
was ten feet away and before I could get to him Luc
had knocked one of them out cold and broken the
other guy's wrist.'

'How lovely,' Lissa said with a raging wail. 'That
really comforts me!'

He grinned. 'Don't worry. I haven't worried about
Luc since he was twelve years old.'

She looked at him in startled surmise. 'You've known
him that long?'

'I've known him since he was five,' the man said.
'Taught him to sail myself. Taught him to play poker
too.'

'Oh, it was you?' Lissa asked furiously. 'Well, you
should be ashamed of yourself! It would have been
much better if you'd taught him something else.'

'Oh, oh,' the man murmured under his breath. 'Poor
Luc! You're that sort of honey, are you?'

She didn't answer that. After a pause she asked, 'What's your name?'

'They call me Dandy,' he said, offering a calloused hand which totally engulfed her own. He shook her hand firmly.

'I'm Lissa,' she said, and he nodded, the movement of his head in the darkness just visible.

'I know. Luc told me.'

'Does he tell you everything?'

Dandy considered this for a moment. 'Yeah,' he said, then laughed. 'Well, most things. He has to.'

'Why? Do you have a hold over him?' Lissa wasn't sure if she liked this large man with the deep warm voice who had taught Luc to play poker.

Dandy laughed. 'Sort of. I'm his bodyguard.'

'He needs one,' she said, angry again. 'He needs you now. Why aren't you with him?'

'Luc will tell me if he needs me,' Dandy said casually. 'His antennae work too well for him to make a mistake.'

'I never heard of a stockbroker having a bodyguard,' Lissa said snappily.

'A what?' Dandy stopped rowing and stared.

'Isn't he?'

'A stockbroker?' Dandy threw back his head and roared with amusement. 'Is that what he told you?'

Lissa was stiff and cold. 'I knew he was a liar,' she said with fury. 'I should have known better than to believe a word he told me.'

'You should, you should indeed,' Dandy teased her, grinning. 'Luc didn't get his nickname for nothing. You know what they call Lucifer—the father of all lies?'

Lissa dropped her cold face into her shaking hands.

'What am I doing?' she moaned under her breath. 'What have I done?'

She had told herself not to trust Luc. She had warned herself not to jump out of the frying pan into the fire, but on a crazy impulse she had done just that.

She had run away from the threat of Chris's possession and now she was in the power of a man she barely knew, a man who had lied to her and was as ruthless in pursuit of what he wanted as ever Chris would be.

Dandy was laughing. 'A stockbroker,' he muttered, slapping his own knee. 'God damn him—a stockbroker! What will he pull next?'

Lissa was sick with shame and self-disgust. She looked back over her shoulder at the fast disappearing coastline. The lights of the hotel blazed like wildfire in the darkness. The moon had gone behind a bank of thin cloud and the ocean was very dark and silent. The cliffs and trees carved heavy shadows on the sky around the lighted hotel.

'Take me back,' she said huskily, and Dandy stopped laughing to look at her in silence.

'Don't be a dumb bunny,' he said, continuing to row.

'Take me back!'

'Even if I was going to, I couldn't,' Dandy added. 'I haven't got the energy. I'll just about make it to the *Queen*.'

'The *Queen*?' She moistened dry lips to ask that.

'The yacht,' Dandy explained. '*The Queen of Spades*, that's what Luc named her. Daring his luck again. That boy loves to fly in the face of all reason.'

'Boy!' Lissa flung back angrily. 'Boy?'

Dandy chuckled. 'Man, then. Yeah, he's no boy, I guess.'

She settled back in a grim silence and Dandy rowed with slow, effortless strokes. It took so long to reach the yacht that Lissa was half asleep when they finally slipped into the dark shadow of the boat. A voice softly hailed them. A ladder swung from the deck and Dandy hoisted her, his large hands gripping her waist, supporting her as she slipped slightly.

Someone's hand dragged her over the side and she stood there, shivering, the dog under her arm growling with raised hair.

'What's that?' The man who had pulled her aboard stared at Fortuné. 'Where did that come from?'

Dandy appeared, puffing. 'She wouldn't leave the little rat,' he grunted.

'Damn!' the man muttered.

Dandy put an arm around Lissa as she swayed, cold and sick. 'Hey, the little lady is dead on her feet.'

Lissa felt his arms round her and then she was swung up against his chest and carried down a narrow gangway.

She closed her eyes and just gave up. Dandy carried her into a cabin and laid her on a bunk. A moment later she woke up with a cry when she felt him stripping off her sweater. Her hands flailed and she yelled, 'Let me alone!'

'Hey, hey,' Dandy grumbled. 'That sweater's wringing wet. Think I'd meddle with one of Luc's possessions? Come on, now, be a good little girl and let Dandy get you undressed and into bed.'

She opened her eyes wide to search his face and see him clearly for the first time. She saw a broad, grizzled man in his fifties with a head which looked as if it had been carved out of concrete and then weathered by wind and sun. His skin was mahogany, lined and wrinkled, his eyes a light grey. His hair was grey and sparse. His mouth was wide and strong. His ears stuck out at angles from his head. Lissa saw humour, calm self-confidence, kindness in his face.

She relaxed in his hands and Dandy went on taking off her clothes. He might have been a child's nurse. He didn't seem to see her body and he talked reassuringly as he worked.

'You get some sleep now and in the morning we'll be away on the tide. Joe's bringing you some nice hot cocoa—made with tinned milk, I'm afraid, but you won't mind that, will you? That'll help you sleep.'

'I couldn't sleep,' she said drily. 'Not with Luc ashore and in danger.'

'Now just you let us worry over Luc. I told you, the devil looks after his own. Luc will be fine.'

'You don't know,' she cried miserably.

Dandy was folding her like a baby into a warm cocoon of quilt. 'Dandy knows everything,' he told her, grinning down at her. 'All you have to do is remember that and you'll fall asleep like a baby.'

Someone moved behind him and her glance flicked to the newcomer. He grinned at her, winking. 'That's right, miss. Dandy is as close to omniscient as you're likely to meet this side of the pearly gates.'

Dandy offered to cuff him. 'This is Joe,' he told Lissa, removing the mug of cocoa from the young man's hands and handing it to her.

She smiled weakly at Joe and got a grin back. Joe went out and Dandy patted her head, his huge hand light on her hair. 'Drink your cocoa and get some sleep,' he said, going out.

She leant up on one elbow, the folds of the quilt draped around her, and sipped the steaming chocolate drink. There was a thick skin on the top of it, but she was so cold she did not care.

Fortuné had nestled down on the bunk beside her feet, snuggling under the quilt. He was asleep, giving whining little snorts from time to time, his nose pushed against her bare feet.

The yacht swayed on the water and a bell somewhere chimed softly. Lissa looked up at the porthole. Luc would still be playing poker. How long would it be before Chris knew she had gone? Would Luc have time to get away before it was discovered?

He hadn't told her what he meant to do. He hadn't told her anything very much, and what he had told her was lies, she thought. Stockbroker ... Dandy had roared at the very idea, amused by Luc's lie.

Lissa wasn't amused. Why had Luc told her that? To soothe her and reassure her?

She felt a cold shiver of dismay as she faced her own future. She had voluntarily given herself into the hands of a man who had lied to her, a man with a background as troubled and murky as Chris. Luc was just as dangerous, just as unscrupulous, just as amoral. He was a pirate, a professional gambler, and she had been crazy to trust him.

Finishing her cocoa she put down her mug and lay back in the bunk. She watched the swaying lamp above her, her eyes following that slow pendulum intently.

How could she sleep? She was torn between fear for Luc and anger with him.

Her eyes were heavy and her brain moved slowly,

trying to sort out what she could do, unable to think clearly about anything.

She was growing warm at last and she felt her tense muscles beginning to relax as heat crept over her body. There wasn't a sound from anywhere on the yacht. Were all the men asleep? How could they even consider sleep when Luc was in danger? She turned on the pillow, yawning. She couldn't possibly sleep. She couldn't, possibly.

CHAPTER SEVEN

LISSA stirred, still fathoms deep in sleep, but disturbed by several things which had only just begun to penetrate her drowsy mind. The scent of bacon drifted around her, the delicious odour of coffee. She moved under the warm quilt, her nose wrinkling.

Someone laughed and her lids flew open. Sunlight struck across her unguarded eyes. She blinked, shifting in the bunk, and became aware of a difference in the movements of the yacht.

She sat up, giving a stifled cry, and then stared in disbelief as she saw the tall figure lounging on the end of her bunk.

'Luc!' The sight of him sent a wave of sick relief through her. His lean dark face was expressionless as he watched her and her smile vanished as she realised something else.

She was naked, the quilt having dropped back from her body as she sat up. Colour flared into her face. She grabbed the quilt and wound it around herself with a shaking hand.

'Slept well, did you?' Luc enquired silkily, watching her with open amusement.

'I think there was something in that cocoa,' she accused, and saw his mouth twitch at the edges.

'Dandy thought you'd be better off asleep,' he said in half admission.

'He had no right to do that!'

Luc shrugged, his wide shoulders moving easily under the cotton sweater he wore.

Lissa took a long, painful breath. 'What happened last night?'

'I played poker,' he drawled. Getting off the bunk, he moved away and turned with a tray in his hands. 'Your breakfast,' he said.

'I couldn't eat anything! Tell me what happened last night, Luc.'

He came across to her and placed the tray across her knees. Lissa glared at him. 'How am I supposed to eat it like this?'

'You can't,' he agreed. 'You'll have to come out of your cocoon.' His eyes glinted teasingly at her. 'I don't mind watching.'

Her cheeks burnt. 'Will you please find me some clothes?'

Luc grinned at her, but went over to a chest and came back with a loose, very large white sweater. He tossed it to her. 'This do?'

'Please turn your back,' she said with dignity.

'Shutting the stable door after the horse has bolted, aren't you?' he asked softly.

'Please,' she muttered.

He shrugged and swung away. Lissa hurriedly dragged the sweater over her head. The tray rocked alarmingly. She sat up, safely covered, and Luc turned to survey her. His grin made her flush increase.

'Ten sizes too big, but you look very sexy in it,' he informed her.

'The yacht's moving,' she said, ignoring that remark.

'We've been under way for hours. We thought we'd

let you sleep until we were safely out of reach of Brandon's pursuit.'

'Are we?' she asked nervously.

'We are,' Luc nodded. His eyes probed her face. 'Sorry? Or relieved?'

She looked down at the tray, trembling slightly.

'Eat your breakfast while it's hot,' Luc urged.

Lissa began to eat, her stomach protesting hungrily at the delicious scent of the food. 'Tell me what happened,' she said with her head bent.

Luc strolled to the porthole and looked out. 'I told you I'd beat him hands down and I did.'

'You won a lot of money?'

'He plays too wildly. He started off quite cool, but he went to pieces towards the end.'

Poor Chris, she thought, shuddering.

'I took him apart,' said Luc, his voice silky.

'Don't,' Lissa whispered through trembling lips. Tears pricked at her eyes and a salty taste filled her mouth.

'Tears for Brandon?' Luc asked in a hard, sarcastic voice. 'If you'd stayed you would have shed them for yourself.'

Huskily, Lissa said: 'Whatever he's done ...'

'You still love him? I gathered that last night,' Luc bit out. 'Why didn't you stay with him, then?' He didn't wait for her to answer, his voice flaying her, cold and tipped with steel. 'I'll tell you why, shall I? You knew damned well I was right about him and you ran because you knew that sort of life wasn't what you wanted. But you still hanker for him, don't you? I realised that when you kissed him last night.'

Lissa stared, her face distraught, tears on her lashes.

Luc smiled at her icily. 'Very touching scene it was, too. I thought at the time it meant you'd decided to stay with him. He was purring like a stroked cat after you'd gone, grinning at me triumphantly.' His mouth twisted. 'Brandon knew we were playing for more than money, and after you kissed him he thought he'd already won. He couldn't keep his mind on the game after that—he was sweating to get to you. You may not have meant to, but you were helping me.'

Lissa shivered. She had gone in there like Judas to give Chris the kiss of betrayal, but Luc was looking at her with icy distaste and she knew he would not believe her if she told him why she had gone to the gambling rooms.

'It must have been a hard decision to make,' Luc remarked in that chilly voice. 'Poor Lissa!'

She drank some of the coffee, her head bent, not even trying to answer.

When she felt able to speak quite steadily she asked: 'Where are we going?'

'Does it matter? England, eventually. But I'm in no hurry.' Luc crossed to the door and opened it. He looked back at her, his smile malicious. 'I intend to enjoy the voyage.'

He went out and the door snapped shut. Lissa stared at it, her body trembling. Luc had not needed to expand on that cryptic little remark; his narrowed eyes had enforced it.

She had had a choice to make, and she had chosen on driven impulse, but when she contemplated what might lie ahead of her, her stomach turned over in humiliation and shame.

There was nowhere for her to run to—she was imprisoned on a yacht with a blue ocean around her and no choice but to submit to whatever Luc demanded.

The inevitability of her own submission was not the worst thing preying on her mind. It was the shameful truth that Luc wouldn't even need to use force. He could take her, whenever he chose, because she wouldn't even put up a fight. The thought of belonging to Chris had finally become intolerable to her. His lovemaking had always alarmed and disturbed her, but even the contemplation of Luc's lovemaking could send waves of weakening heat around her whole body.

She wondered how long it had taken Chris to realise she had gone and to guess who had taken her away.

Chris had lost last night. He might be the ruthless thug Luc had called him, but Lissa had known him for so many years. She covered her face with her hands, feeling sick with pain. Poor Chris! She didn't know if he loved her, but he would have lost face with his men, he would be feeling humiliated, angry. Old affection for him made her wish he had not had to lose quite so openly.

Fortuné was finishing her breakfast greedily. Lissa put an arm around his neck and hugged him. Burying her face in his coat, she muttered to him, 'I despise myself, Fortuné. I'm crazy!'

Fortuné licked whatever part of her he could reach, aware of her need for comfort and ready to supply it in his own fashion. She laughed, tears on her lashes, then jumped as someone knocked loudly on the cabin door.

'Come in,' she quavered huskily.

Dandy put his grizzled head around the door. 'Morning, princess. Your ladyship's clothes.' He had them over his arm, neatly pressed. 'All present and correct,' he told her, draping them over the end of the bunk. He reached a long arm over and plucked the dog out of her arms. 'While you get dressed I'll take the little dog for a walk.' He held Fortuné up by his neck and grinned at him as he growled. 'What sort of dog d'you call that?'

'He's a poodle,' Lissa said indignantly.

'Poodle, is he? Come on, horrible, Dandy is going to show you the deck.'

When he had gone she slid out of bed. The cabin was large and elegantly furnished, she found on inspection. There was a narrow shower cubicle in one corner of it and the furniture was all fitted so that it did not shift as the yacht rolled with the waves. However Luc made his money, it was clear he had it. Lissa couldn't even begin to guess how much this yacht was worth. She had never seen one like it.

It was, she thought wryly, like a floating hotel. Last night in the shock and depression of her arrival she had barely taken in any of it, but she had retained an impression of size which had stayed with her.

A long, narrow mirror lined a wardrobe. Lissa studied herself in it. The loose sweater fell to her bare thighs. She looked dishevelled and very flushed. Grimacing at her own reflection, she pulled off the sweater and went into the cubicle to shower.

When she had dried herself she dressed in her own sweater and the neatly pressed jeans. They had, she suspected, been washed overnight. She made her bed and tidied up the cabin before she went on deck.

She could hear the low throbbing of the engine

vibrating through the timbers. At a glance she could only guess at the number of cabins, but there were a row of doors leading off the gangway running from the base of the steps. Everything gleamed with polish, the wood, metal and glass immaculate.

When she emerged on deck she found Fortuné being dragged to and fro on the end of a long thin rope. Dandy grinned at her. 'Seasick,' he told her. 'He doesn't like the sea much, does he?'

Fortuné was whining, trying to get back to her.

'Take him below,' said a voice behind her, and she stiffened, swinging to face Luc.

Dandy picked the little dog up and marched off with him. Luc met her eyes coolly. 'He'll feel better below. He won't notice the motion so much.'

She moved to the rail and leaned on it, watching the flying white wake streaking behind them. Luc moved to stand beside her. She looked at his long, brown hands on the iron rail and her throat filled with dry tension.

'How did you manage to get away?' she asked huskily.

'How could he stop me?' Luc asked with a grim smile. 'I had a car waiting at the hotel and a boat waiting in the town. He thought I was making a getaway with the money I'd won.' He laughed. 'He didn't realise precisely what stakes we were playing for.'

Lissa shivered. 'He won't come after us, will he?'

Luc glanced over his shoulder at the empty blue water. 'Even if he did he wouldn't catch us. The *Queen* has too much of a headway.'

'I shan't feel safe until I'm in England,' said Lissa, and Luc gave her a long, sardonic smile.

'I'm sure you won't,' he drawled, and there was a threat in the softness of his voice.

She shifted uneasily at the sound of it. Luc turned to lean his back on the rail, glancing up at the burning, untiring sun. 'Why don't you take a lounger and sun-bathe for an hour? I've got some work to do.'

He went below and Lissa stretched out on the pad-ded lounger which Dandy put up for her on the deck. Occasionally one of the crew came up and moved around, but although they always gave her a polite nod they did not speak to her. She counted four of them and wondered how many more there were on the yacht.

Dandy called her down to lunch just as she was falling asleep under the spell of wind and sun. Flushed and drowsy, she went down to wash and followed Dandy to the cabin two doors down from her own. She found herself eating alone with Luc at a polished rose-wood table guarded at the edges with low rims of silver which stopped things sliding off the table.

They ate well-cooked and elegantly served food of which Lissa barely tasted a morsel. She ate it but she only vaguely realised what she was eating. Luc was quiet and when their eyes met she could not see a flicker of expression in the dark blue ones opposite her.

After lunch Luc suggested a tour of the yacht. Lissa followed him from cabin to cabin, surprised by the luxury of the surroundings, puzzled by the size of it.

'What do you do with the yacht while you're in London?' she asked.

He shrugged. 'She either lies up or I lend her to friends. Dandy sails her for them. I keep the crew on throughout the year. I know them all and I don't want to lose them. If you're going to spend time cooped up with someone on a yacht you need to be sure you're going to like and trust them.'

Lissa stood by the porthole in his cabin staring out at the sunlit water. 'You're very rich, aren't you?' Her voice came thin and dry like smoke.

Luc didn't answer for a moment, then he said in a flat voice, 'Yes. Very.'

'You lied to me about your job, didn't you? You don't deal in stocks and shares.'

'Yes, I do,' he said.

She swung then, her face angry. 'Dandy laughed when I asked him if you were a stockbroker.'

Luc's mouth flicked sideways in grim amusement. 'Did he, damn him?'

'What do you do? Who are you?' she insisted.

'I am myself,' Luc said calmly. 'That's all you need to know.'

'Are you a criminal? Are you a gangster like Chris?' she asked feverishly. 'I've let you talk me into leaving Chris, but what do I know about you?'

Luc surveyed her without speaking, his face taut and set. 'You don't know anything,' he agreed. 'You're going to have to take me on trust, Lissa. You've little choice.'

'Why won't you tell me anything about yourself?' she demanded in rising tones.

'Why should I?' Luc asked drily. 'If you can't bring yourself to accept me without some sort of affidavit for my character, you're going to have to grin and bear it.'

'I don't trust you,' she muttered hoarsely.

'So I see,' Luc drawled.

'You can't find that surprising!'

'You trusted Brandon until I made you see him as he really was,' Luc came back tightly.

'I've known Chris all my life. He's looked after me and cared for me.'

'And wanted you,' Luc said in a low harsh voice.

Lissa bit her lip and looked at the floor.

'You were ready to give yourself to him without knowing a damned thing about him. You can do the same for me,' said Luc, and her throat hurt as she swallowed.

She couldn't look up or answer. Luc waited, watching her.

'No comment?' he asked coolly. 'Very wise.'

'What comment do you expect me to make? A remark like that doesn't deserve an answer.'

His face was hard, his eyes narrowed. 'You came with me—you knew what that would mean.'

Lissa felt a shiver run down her spine. 'You offered to help me get away from Chris. I didn't realise you were putting a price tag on your help,' she said contemptuously.

Luc laughed grimly. 'Oh, you knew all right. You may be a little naïve, but you aren't totally stupid. I made no secret of what I would expect, and you understood the situation, however much you may deny it now.'

'I might have known you were every bit as much a ruthless swine as Chris!'

'You might, indeed,' he drawled. 'Poor Lissa—what a predicament!'

The unhidden mockery stiffened her spine. She glared at him, her eyes alive with anger. 'I'm glad you think it's so funny!'

He leaned against the cabin wall, his arms folded. 'You can always swim back to him. It isn't very far—

around seventy miles, I suppose. But you're a good swimmer, aren't you? If the sharks don't get you, it won't take more than a few days.'

'Given a choice between you and the sharks, I might well prefer the sharks,' Lissa muttered through her teeth.

His blue eyes hardened. 'Ah, but I'm afraid you won't be given the choice. I've got you and I'm keeping you.'

Very flushed, she said furiously: 'You have not got me!'

'It's only a matter of time,' Luc pointed out silkily. He moved and she leapt back towards the door, her nerves jangling. Luc laughed, giving her a wry look. 'Don't get uptight just yet. I'm in no hurry. Love in the afternoon is a taste I've never acquired.' He opened the door and gave her a derisory little bow. 'After you.'

Lissa shot through the door like a scalded cat. Luc came after her and said lightly: 'I've got some work to do. Why don't you relax on the deck again? I'll see you later.'

She stayed on the deck, as he had suggested, but there was no relaxation involved. She was tense and disturbed as she watched the water creaming along in their wake. Once Dandy wandered up to talk to her, but most of the time she spent alone with her thoughts, and she did not enjoy them very much.

The sun went down with that abrupt and startling rush which always signalled nightfall. Dandy smiled at her as she came down into the cabin to eat the light, evening meal. 'Enjoying your cruise?'

She pretended to laugh. 'Very much.'

Dandy went out and Luc eyed her sardonically. He knew she was lying and the blue eyes told her as much.

When they had eaten and Dandy had vanished, Luc put a record on the turntable fitted into the wall of the cabin. Lissa nervously sat on the leather couch which, like the rest of the furniture, was stabilised so that it did not shift with the motion of the yacht.

'I'm rather tired,' she said huskily. 'The sea air, I suppose. I think I'll go to bed early.'

Luc sank down beside her, his arm sliding along the back of the couch behind her. 'That sounds promising.'

She sat upright, giving him an angry look. 'I've no intention of going to bed with you, Mr Ferrier, so you can forget it!'

He laughed. 'What an optimist you are!' His fingers had touched the edge of her sweater sleeve. They slid in under the cuff and stroked her wrist. It was a tantalisingly intimate little movement and the hairs on the back of her neck prickled with awareness.

'Brandon never even got to first base with you, did he?' Luc murmured, his body moving closer. Lissa tried to shift away, but he followed, his thigh pressing alongside her own. 'I felt quite sorry for him the night I followed the pair of you down to the beach.'

She threw him an accusing glance. 'I heard you lurking about in the trees.'

His mouth curled. 'Was that why you were so reluctant with him? He was going crazy and it was obvious you were keeping him at bay. Was that for my benefit?'

'I didn't know it was you. I just heard movements and then when we walked into you, I guessed you had been eavesdropping.'

'I was curious,' he admitted calmly. His hand was behind her head now, playing with her hair, twisting it round a finger and then releasing it.

'Curious about what?' she asked, feeling that fondling hand with extreme wariness.

'You,' he said with a wry smile. 'You were puzzling me. I couldn't make up my mind which image of you to believe. One minute you were blushing like a schoolgirl, the next you were on stage singing very sexy songs and giving the audience come-hither smiles.'

'I did nothing of the kind!' she burst out, glaring at him.

His fingers wriggled under her hair and lightly stroked along her nape, sending quivers of reaction down her spine.

'Stop that,' she whispered unsteadily.

Luc smiled at her, mockery in the blue eyes. 'Why should I? I'm enjoying it.' She began to get up and his arm fenced her between his body and the end of the couch, forcing her to lean back. 'Stay where you are,' he commanded, and her eyes fell away from his.

'Where was I?' he murmured. 'Ah, yes—Brandon. From what I overheard on the beach that night I gathered with some surprise that he hadn't yet managed to get you into bed.'

Lissa's face burned. 'Mind your own business!'

'I could see that Brandon was almost at the end of his tether. It was equally obvious that you were having no problems at all in resisting him. The poor devil had to work like mad to get as much as a kiss out of you.'

Lissa did not want to remember Chris's aroused excitement. She gave Luc a cold look. 'Can we change the subject?'

'No, we can't,' Luc said forcibly. 'I'm trying to get

you to admit something and you're going to listen.'

'What do you want me to admit? That I didn't go to bed with Chris? Very well, I didn't, but it still isn't your business.'

'I don't need to be told you didn't, I was already certain of it,' Luc said curtly. 'No, Lissa. What you're going to admit is that you were never even tempted to give in to him.' He paused and she said coldly:

'So?'

'But when I made love to you it took me about five minutes to break down those barriers of yours.'

He was watching her intently as he said the last words. He saw the deep, betraying colour sweep up her face, the widened shock in the green eyes. Lissa hurriedly looked away from his scrutiny.

'So didn't it?' he asked softly.

'You didn't give me much option,' she muttered, her head bent.

He laughed quietly. 'Don't lie. Brandon was equally insistent and it got him precisely nowhere. It never had, had it? That wasn't the first time he'd been going spare without so much as rousing a flicker in you.'

She drew a quick, harsh breath.

'That's why he had hung on so patiently, month after month, when he could have married you long ago. He knew damned well he wasn't getting to you. You said you loved him and there was nobody else around, but every time he touched you he knew you weren't feeling a thing.'

It was true. She had been alarmed rather than aroused, worried rather than excited, when Chris tried to make love to her. And Chris had known, of course. He was too experienced not to know.

She lifted her head and stared at Luc, frowning. 'Can we talk about something else? I just want to forget about Chris.'

'Not before you face facts,' Luc insisted flatly. 'You were never in love with him. You may have thought you were, but it was just old affection. I don't want you carrying any images of Brandon around inside your head. He was a dangerous thug and if you'd married him you would have led a miserable life.'

'If I hadn't realised that, I wouldn't have left,' she said huskily.

'But you still haven't entirely faced up to it,' Luc retorted. 'Or you would never have come into the gaming rooms to kiss him goodbye. You had a romantic picture of him and even though you're disillusioned about him now, you still feel something.' He slid a hand under her chin and lifted her face. 'It was all an illusion, Lissa. Your subconscious knew that. That's why you would never let him make love to you. You didn't want him.' He drew a long, unsteady breath. 'But you want me.'

'No,' she said hurriedly, before his mouth closed demandingly over hers and silenced her.

Her heart began beating so fast she felt giddy. The yacht seemed suddenly to be going round in circles, making her head spin, her mind dissolve. Her ears were deafened by the rush and roar of her own blood.

The insistent pressure of his mouth, the slow caressing movements of his hands as they slid under her sweater and moulded her body softly between them, made her shudder in fierce response.

She tried to wrench her head away, but Luc's hand fixed it there while his lips forced hers to part and

moistly invaded her mouth. Hating herself, helpless
to do anything to halt her own response, she trembled
in his arms. Her arms moved to enclose his head. She
began to return his kisses with a heat which flew out
of her control within minutes.

Luc's kisses deepened, heated, commanded more and
more response. Lissa made no further attempt to halt
him. When his fingers brushed lightly, coaxingly down
her skin she moaned, her own hand tracing the arch
of his back, tunnelling beneath his sweater, her fingertips feeling the tiny hairs, the flexed muscles, the bone
and sinew beneath the smooth skin.

Her exploring fingers found a small scar marring the
back of his shoulder and ran over it, following it. Luc
lifted his head, his breath coming raggedly. 'A fight
with a shark,' he breathed, laughing.

'Why are you so reckless?' Lissa groaned.

'It's my nature,' he told her casually. 'Take me as you
find me, Lissa.' He paused and their eyes met. 'Are you
going to take me, Lissa?' he asked in that husky, im-
peded voice.

He slid his hand gently up her body. She felt the
cool trail of his fingertips on her breast and her body
winced with a pleasure that was like pain. Luc outlined
the high, soft peak with delicate brushes of his fingers.
She closed her eyes, moaning, and heard him laugh
under his breath.

'Brandon never made you feel like this, did he?' he
asked as he took her mouth again, his lips hard and hot.

She had meant to fight, but it was like fighting life
itself. Everything alive in her craved for what he was
doing. She was only denying herself if she denied him.

His hands travelled down her again. She felt the zip

of her jeans slide down and her body tightened. She pushed Luc's hand away, pulling her head back to exclaim angrily: 'No!'

His hand had slid inside her jeans before she could halt it again. Luc stroked her bare midriff and Lissa shook violently at the warm, intimate caress.

'No?' he whispered, smiling.

She closed her eyes. 'Please, Luc, give me time. You're rushing me.'

'I want to hear you admit you want me,' Luc muttered, his face buried in her throat. He kissed the throbbing pulse which was making it very clear how far he had aroused her. 'You never wanted Brandon, Lissa, but you want me.'

'Yes,' she moaned, giving up the struggle to resist. It was taking all her energy, exhausting her. The tidal beat of passion had too much force in it and she was tired of struggling against it.

Luc gave a long, hoarse sigh of satisfaction. For a long moment he lay still, his lips at her neck, then he sat up and gave her an intent stare.

'Now look at me and let me hear you say that again,' he said in a quiet voice.

Lissa stared at him dazedly. 'What?'

'I'm not touching you now,' he pointed out, lifting his hands to show her. 'I'm not rushing you. Be honest, Lissa. When you came with me you knew what you were doing, didn't you? You weren't just walking out on Brandon, you were choosing me.'

Her eyes moved away; she swallowed painfully.

'Weren't you, Lissa?' he insisted.

'I don't know,' she whispered. 'Why can't you give me time to think? How do I know what I feel?'

'I could tell you,' Luc said drily. 'But I suppose you wouldn't want to hear.' He stood up and moved away. 'You'd better get off to bed.'

She didn't move, staring at the back of his head. Luc looked at her over his shoulder, his face set. 'Alone,' he expanded flatly. 'I've no intention of forcing myself on you tonight.'

With trembling fingers she zipped up her jeans, pulled down her sweater. As she stood up she swayed and Luc turned to support her.

'What's the matter, Lissa?' he asked mockingly. 'Feeling weak?'

She felt a flare of rage as she looked at the smile he was giving her. 'I'm tired,' she said, moving away from him.

'Oh, is that it?'

She didn't bother to reply to that. She made her way to the door and said flatly, 'Goodnight,' as she left the cabin.

She heard him murmur 'Goodnight,' and closed the door. Her own cabin seemed very small and very quiet. She undressed and got into her bunk. There was no sign of Fortuné. Dandy must have him in his quarters, she recognised, and guessed that that had been Luc's idea. His plans for the night had not included the presence of her dog.

Lissa turned on to her face and hated herself. Her few token efforts to resist him had been easily controlled. She had been a pushover for him. Why am I such a fool? she asked herself, and had no answer to give.

Chris's urgent lovemaking had merely worried her. Luc somehow managed to light a quick-burning fuse.

inside her every time he touched her.

How long would it take them to get to England? She had little money and she knew nobody in England. She was as much at Luc's mercy as she had been at Chris's. If Luc could beat down all her weak struggles in one evening, what chance had she got of holding out against him until they reached England? And even if she did, what was she going to do once she left the yacht?

CHAPTER EIGHT

FAINT white ribbons of light drifted across the cabin
when Lissa opened her eyes next morning. They had
sailed into mist, and whoever was in charge of the yacht
had switched on an intermittent hooter which gave
hoarse sighs every now and again. Lissa lay listening
to them, staring at the ceiling. There was a strong swell
this morning. The yacht flounced like an angry woman
and she wasn't sure her stomach altogether approved
of the motion.

There was a tap at her door. 'Come in,' she called in
a slightly nervous voice.

Dandy appeared with a tray. 'Morning, princess,' he
said cheerfully, shooting a quick look at her. 'Misty, but
it's beginning to clear.'

'The boat keeps rolling about,' Lissa complained.

Dandy grinned. 'You wait until we're right out in the
Atlantic!'

She made a face. 'I think I'd rather get off now.'

He eyed her consideringly. 'Feeling queasy, are we?'

'A little,' she admitted.

Dandy glanced down at the tray. 'Want this?' He un-
covered a plate of bacon and egg and Lissa turned her
head away, her nostrils wrinkling at the odour.

'Not much,' she muttered, swallowing. 'I'm sorry.'

'You've got to eat something,' Dandy assured her.
'Have some dry toast.'

She was reluctant to eat anything, but he insisted

that she nibble a little toast and drink some of his strong coffee. 'Little dog slept with me,' he told her as he walked back to the door. 'He's up on deck getting some exercise on a rope.'

Lissa lay in the bunk for half an hour slowly adjusting to the pitch and swell. When she felt strong enough she got up and dressed.

As she emerged from the shelter of the gangway the wind almost lifted her like a doll. She grabbed at the rail and heard voices.

Luc's rose curtly. 'Mind your own damned business!'

'Don't take that tone with me, boy,' Dandy growled. His eyes flicked towards her over Luc's shoulder and his face changed. 'Morning, miss. Managed to get up, did you? Good girl!'

Luc did not turn. He stood with his back to her and Dandy glanced at him before shrugging and walking away.

Lissa looked at the straight, lithe body turned away from her, then she walked to the rail and looked out over the ocean. She heard Luc move, heard the slow fall of his steps. He came to a stop beside her and his stare probed her profile, reading her mood in the tightness of her skin.

'Dandy says you felt sick this morning. Better now?'

'Much, thank you.'

'You've never done any sailing before?'

'Only a little around the island.'

'I'm afraid it will get rougher as we move further into the Atlantic,' he warned her.

'So Dandy said.'

There was a pause, then he asked drily: 'What's the matter, Lissa?'

'Nothing.' She did not look round, keeping her eyes fixed on the rise and fall of the grey waters into which they were moving. From the look of the flat horizon Dandy was right—bad weather was waiting for them.

She felt Luc's hand at her waist. His fingers stroked slowly up her back and she stiffened. 'Don't do that!'

He ran that exploring hand along her body, ignoring the muffled protest. She swung, stepping away from him. Her green eyes flared at him angrily. 'If you don't leave me alone I'll chuck myself over the side!'

Luc's smile went. He considered her unreadably, his eyes cool. 'Don't make idle threats.'

'I mean it. If you don't keep your hands to yourself from now on I'll jump overboard.'

'Then from now on you'll only be allowed on deck when I'm with you,' Luc bit out coldly. His face was hard, his eyes like blue steel. 'If you're going to make childish threats you must be treated like a child.'

'You can't make me stay below!' Lissa flung back the angry words and the wind whipped them away across the water.

He smiled, a fierce twist of the mouth which had no humour in it. 'Just watch me.'

'You can't keep me locked up for ever,' she retorted. 'At the very first port we come to, I'll attract attention somehow. I'll scream and wave and break the porthole.'

'You won't get the chance, sweetheart,' he promised in a drawl. 'I'll see to that. I'll keep you far too occupied while we're in port to do a damn thing to attract anybody's attention but mine.'

Her face burned at the mockery in his eyes. There was a coldness beneath it which she hated, which made her situation so much worse. Luc intended to make love

to her and his awareness of her inability to stop him,
the cynical coolness of those blue eyes, made her veins
run with ice.

'I must have been insane to imagine I could trust
you,' she accused unsteadily. 'I should have known
you'd make me pay dearly for any help you gave me.'

'You knew what I would expect,' he retorted, the
lines of his face hardening.

'And it doesn't matter whether I want the same thing,
I suppose,' Lissa flung at him, her voice brittle and
hoarse.

His eyes narrowed. 'You want me, Lissa. Stop lying to
yourself.'

The way he watched her made her throat beat with
fever. She moved, but he moved faster. He caught her,
his hand tightening around her wrist in a vice-like grip.

'Are you determined to annoy me? Because if so,
you're on the way to succeeding, Lissa. You may have
been able to play fast and loose with Brandon for
months, but you aren't doing it to me.'

'I'm not playing anything,' she said angrily, looking
at him with defiance. 'Can't you even begin to see it
from my viewpoint?'

'You're not playing games with me!' he bit out.

'Why can't you leave me alone?' Lissa groaned, pulling away.

Luc's blue eyes hardened. He yanked her forward
by her tethered hand and trapped her between his body
and the rail. His other hand jerked back her head and
he kissed her ruthlessly, the wind tangling their hair
and leaving a salt bloom on their skin.

When at last Luc lifted his head he was breathing

heavily. She was trembling, her lips bruised and yielding. The fierce thud of Luc's heart beat next to hers.

She met his blue eyes without trying to avoid them. Her whole body was melting in the passion he had unleashed in her.

'You really get to me, Liss,' he muttered thickly.

His eyes were leaping with the desire she could feel in the hard body pressing against her. It left Lissa so weak she could only just manage to breathe.

Luc straightened, moving away, his breathing slowing. 'You're here and you're staying,' he told her. 'And you're mine. It's too late for you to have second thoughts. If you're regretting Brandon I'm sorry—you made your choice and you must stick with it. I've got you and I'm not giving you up.'

Lissa stared at the deck, her face very flushed.

After a pause Luc said curtly: 'Come below. We'll have some coffee.'

'I feel sick,' she said.

Luc muttered a swear word under his breath. 'Very well,' he added harshly. 'You can go back to your own cabin and stay there.' He took her arm and thrust her back below, pushing her into her cabin with an anger he made no attempt to hide. 'Sulk there as much as you like,' he bit out as he slammed the door and locked it.

Dandy brought her a cup of tea some time later. She heard the key turn and swung, her eyes wary, relaxing as she saw that it was not Luc. Dandy gave her a quick look. She felt he could read the misery and fear in her face and hurriedly pulled herself together.

'Tea, princess,' he said, handing her a large bright yellow mug. She took it, murmuring a grateful word.

'That's my mug, princess,' he said, smiling.

'I'm honoured.'

'Not often I lend my mug to people,' he agreed. He sat down on the edge of her bunk and surveyed her. 'You look as if you need a good strong whisky rather than tea.'

'I don't drink,' she said, shaking her head.

His grin stretched from ear to ear. 'Something told me you might not—how old are you, ladybird?'

'Twenty.'

His face tightened. 'Twenty,' he repeated, grimacing.

Lissa sipped her tea, not meeting his eyes. Dandy sighed. 'He's wild and sometimes he's reckless, but you can trust him,' he told her gently. 'I'd trust him to hell and back.'

'You're not a woman!'

Dandy laughed shortly. 'No. All the same, I've never known him hurt anybody if he could avoid it.'

Lissa remembered Luc's ruthless oppression of her body on deck earlier, the unleashed violence with which he had kissed her, and she didn't answer.

'He has a romantic streak,' Dandy went on slowly. 'It comes out in odd ways. When he gets bored with the city we take off like a bat out of hell and sail in search of excitement. Ever since he was a boy he's needed to find wider horizons. He generates a lot of adrenalin and he can't use enough of it in his work.'

'He does work?'

Dandy grinned. 'Like a dog for most of the year—a lot of people depend on him.

She swallowed. 'Is he married?'

'No,' Dandy said firmly, and she believed him.

Her body sagged in relief. She had been half afraid

that Luc might well turn out to be married. 'What sort of work does he do?'

'Don't ask me,' said Dandy, shrugging. 'Tedious stuff in the City. I've never been involved in that side of his life. The wife and I run his home for him and when I'm not there, I'm on the boat. Luc keeps his own counsel. If he confides in me he's always very discreet.'

Lissa met his eyes wryly and knew that Luc had warned Dandy not to tell her anything. Dandy was lying when he said he didn't know anything about Luc's work.

He flushed slightly, getting up. 'I just wanted to tell you to trust him, princess. Luc doesn't like it when he isn't trusted. He has a lot of pride. Where his emotions are involved, he can be as stubborn as the devil.'

'Lucifer,' she said huskily.

Dandy laughed. 'That's what they call him—those who don't know him.'

'What about those who do know him?' Lissa asked with a painful little smile. 'What do they call him?'

Dandy laughed. 'I've called him every name under the sun,' he admitted, moving to the door. 'But I'd still trust him with my life.'

Would he trust Luc with his wife, though, Lissa thought, if his wife happened to be attractive? Dandy closed the door. She heard the key turn again. Whatever Dandy thought about Luc, he was still obeying his instructions. She had a strong idea that Dandy did not approve of the way Luc was behaving, but he was doing as Luc ordered, all the same.

She read a paperback which she had found in the cabin. Time passed very slowly and the sea was getting rough, the wind howling around them as they battled their way through choppy seas.

It was one o'clock when Dandy came back. 'Lunch time,' he told her cheerfully. She followed him to the other cabin and found Luc there, pouring wine, the quick sideways glint of his blue eyes skating over her before he looked back at the glass he was filling.

When Dandy had served them and gone Luc watched Lissa picking at the food on her plate for a moment before he said curtly: 'Stop sulking.'

'I'm not.'

'A damned good imitation, then,' he flung back. 'You're here, and you're with me—and sulking isn't going to change a thing.' He flung a hand towards her wine glass. 'Try some—it may soften you up a bit.'

'Trying to get me drunk?' she asked sarcastically.

'Don't be so damned ridiculous,' Luc snapped. 'One glass of wine isn't going to make you keel over.'

She sipped the wine, avoiding his eyes. Luc waited for another moment then drank some of his own. 'Now eat,' he said roughly.

'I'm not very hungry.' She heard the intake of his breath and added quickly, 'I'm not! The sea's so rough.'

'It will get rougher, I'm afraid,' he said, glancing at the porthole.

Lissa bit her lower lip nervously. 'Will it?'

He gave her a sudden, gentle smile. 'Don't worry— we're safe enough. The boat's well stabilised. She'll weather the storm. We've been through worse than this, I assure you.' He dropped his eyes to her plate. 'Try to eat something, though. You'll find it helps to have food in your stomach.' His smile appeared again, amused and teasing. 'It settles you. Another form of stabilising.'

'I'm not sure I believe you,' she said wryly, but she forced herself to eat a little of the well-cooked food.

Luc allowed her to leave most of the meal. As they got up she said pleadingly: 'I'm so tired of being shut in that cabin—can't I go on deck?'

'It's blowing a gale out there,' Luc pointed out.

'I'd rather be windblown than stuffy!'

He grinned. 'Hang on, then—I'll find you some waterproofs.' He vanished and came back with a vivid yellow waterproof jacket and hood. 'This should fit you.'

Lissa wriggled into it and he laughed at her as she tied the cords at the jacket neck. 'You look absurd,' he told her. 'It's far too big for you. But at least you'll be dry.'

They struggled up on deck to find the wind howling like a banshee and rain sleeting across their faces. The waterproof hung down below Lissa's knees and Luc roared with laughter at her as she fought her way around the deck, the wind tugging at the hood and blowing storm-tossed strands of her hair across her face.

After a few minutes Luc insisted that she had had enough and must go below again. 'You don't want to be sick,' he pointed out.

In her cabin she stripped off the waterproof and handed it to him. Her face was glowing with colour and heat, her hair a wild mop. Luc stood watching her as she brushed it into some semblance of tidiness.

He tossed the waterproof on a chair and moved behind her. In the small mirror their eyes met. Lissa looked at him warily, her body stiffening.

'Don't,' she begged.

He dropped his chin on her shoulder, his lips brushing her neck. 'Don't what?'

'Luc!'

'Mmm?' The slow sensual movement of his mouth was making her skin shiver with pleasure, and that made her angry.

She stepped away and his hands shot out to pull her back against him, his arms around her waist. She trembled as she felt the tense hardness of his body behind her.

'Stop fighting me, Lissa,' he murmured, burrowing his face into her hair until his mouth was sliding along her exposed nape. 'You don't hate it when I touch you. I know you say you do, but your body tells me something very different.'

'My body's a liar, then!'

'No, Lissa, you're the liar,' he retorted.

She shook her head angrily. His hands slid up a second later and closed over her breasts in a possessive gesture, the exploring fingers making her heart beat far too fast and far too painfully.

'Let me go,' she whispered, pushing his hands down. Luc spun her violently and clamped her against him in a hard embrace she could not break, his thigh forced against her own, his hands on her back holding her captive.

Lissa's anger hardened inside her as she met the determined blue eyes. She stared back at him, her mouth straightening to a level, stubborn line. 'I won't go to bed with you, Luc. I ran away from Chris because I refused to let anyone manipulate me and use me, and

I'm not going to let you do it. Chris was never in love with me—he just wanted to take me to bed, too. He saw me as some sort of possession—a thing he wanted, which he was prepared to wait for if he had to—and you see me the same way, too. I'm sick of men grabbing at me! I'm a person, not a thing. I wasn't making idle threats about jumping overboard. I mean every word.' Her voice had risen and quickened as she spoke, her anger flooding her face with hot colour, her eyes burning. 'I'd rather be dead than find myself in your bed. The very idea makes me sick!'

Luc listened, watching her, his face tightening and chilling. When she had broken off the last words with a breathless half-sob he dropped his arms from around her and moved away. Lissa stood, shaking, rigid and cold. Luc walked to the door and opened it.

She watched him go out. The door shut. Lissa's rigidity collapsed in a storm of bitter, scalding tears. She stood with her hands over her face, weeping helplessly.

She had meant everything she said to him, but she still felt drained and sick at having had to say it. Luc had not protested at her accusation that he didn't love her. He had had that much honesty. If she had let him talk her into bed she would have hated herself later and she was glad he had gone. Her tears were inexplicable.

CHAPTER NINE

THE weather worsened as they moved deeper into the Atlantic. Lissa had to stay in her cabin, but now it was not because Luc insisted on it but because she was too sick to move from her bunk.

Luc took the mountainous seas and fierce gales in his stride. Lissa had somehow expected him to be impatient with her over her illness, but he was gentle and sympathic during the whole period. When she whispered an apology to him he smiled at her, shaking his head. 'Don't be silly. It happens to us all.'

It did not happen to him. His skin was as cool and his eyes as clear as ever. Lissa envied him his ability to survive the rolling and tossing of the boat.

She had never felt so dreadful in her whole life. She lay in her bunk, feverish, her head thudding like a hammer, the cabin swirling around her. Luc was with her a good deal of the time. When he left, Dandy appeared. There was comfort in having someone with her and she lost all consciousness of Luc except as the man who dealt calmly with her appalling sickness, wiped her hot face with a damp cool washcloth, murmured soothingly to her when she cried afterwards.

Later, she never knew how long that period lasted. She slept finally for hours and while she was asleep the yacht passed into quiet waters and the winds and rain vanished.

When she did open her eyes again, the cabin lay still

and calm around her. Sunlight gleamed on the polished wood surfaces. Lissa lay and felt the gentle rocking of the boat. She was empty and drained yet oddly content, languidly unwilling to move.

Suddenly she heard an eerie shriek and sat up, startled. The porthole was briefly darkened by the flash of a wing.

Gulls, she thought in astonishment, and slid out of the bunk. As she padded to look out, the door opened behind her. She looked over her shoulder and Luc gave her a smile.

'You're awake! How do you feel?'

'Much better, thank you. I thought I heard a gull.'

'I expect you did—there's one circling around us and hoping for something to eat.'

'Are we near land?' she asked.

'That depends what you call near. I suppose we're around fifty miles off Plymouth.'

She felt shock streak along her nerves. 'Oh,' she said weakly, and a grey depression came down over her. Soon she would be able to leave the yacht, say goodbye to Luc and his threatening attentions and she told herself she was relieved. The peculiar sick misery in the pit of her stomach was merely alarm at the prospect of finding a job, somewhere to live, facing a new life.

Luc was watching her, his face unreadable.

She suddenly realised that she was in the thick flannel pyjama jacket which Dandy had lent her when her own nightclothes ran out during her sickness. The jacket was massive, far too big for her, and she felt ridiculous in it. She climbed back into the bunk, very flushed.

Luc gave a sudden grin. 'What's up now? After

nursing you for the last few days it's a bit late for you
to become prudish.'

'I feel like a clown in this jacket,' she said wryly.

He laughed. 'You look very appealing in it.'

She pleated the sheet with her fingers. 'Thank you
for being so kind and understanding when I was ill.
I'm sorry I was such a nuisance to you.'

'You weren't a nuisance,' Luc said flatly.

'Thank you, anyway.' She glanced up at him. 'When
will we get to England?'

'Tomorrow.' He said the word shortly. 'You've got
your passport?'

She nodded. 'My father made sure I kept a British
passport and I've always renewed it when it ran out.'

'Good. That should make it easier.' Luc paused.
'What plans did you have for when we arrive? Have
you any relatives in England?'

'None that I know of,' she said slowly. 'I shall go to
London and try to get a job.'

'You have some money with you?'

She chewed her lower lip, flushing. 'A little.'

'How much?'

She shrugged. 'Enough to keep me until I find a job.'

'How much?' he insisted.

When she told him he stared at her and gave a short,
angry bark of laughter. 'My God, girl, that won't keep
you for more than two days in London!'

'I'll manage,' she muttered, her head bent.

'You've no idea what you're talking about,' Luc shot
back at her tersely. 'London isn't a little village, you
know. You're in for quite a cultural shock when you
first arrive and being penniless into the bargain will
make it worse.'

'I thought I could get work in a hotel,' said Lissa, still not looking at him. 'After all, that will give me somewhere to live, and I do know all about hotels.'

Luc moved to the porthole and stared out, his hands thrust into his pockets. 'I can't let you wander off alone.'

'I'm responsible for myself!'

He laughed harshly. 'I wish I could believe that. You'd walk straight into some sort of fix and I'd go crazy not knowing what was happening to you.'

Her heart missed a beat. She didn't answer, staring at her own fingers as they fidgeted with the sheet.

'I can't let you do it, Lissa,' he told her roughly.

'You can't stop me.'

He swung, his face fixed in a frowning mask. 'I know I've handled this all wrong, but you've got to trust me, Lissa. At least let me take you to my home for a few days while you find yourself work and a place to live.'

'No.' Her mouth was stiff and stubborn and he watched her with a barely controlled impatience, his body shifting restlessly.

'You're being stupid,' he bit out. His mouth twisted and the blue eyes held sardonic irritation. 'Do you want my word that I won't try to rape you?'

Her colour rushed up in a blinding heat and she glared at him. 'Maybe I do! I wouldn't put it past you.'

She saw that he did not like that. His face tightened. But he said coolly enough: 'Very well, you have my word. I shall not try to rape you. Is that sufficiently reassuring?' He turned and walked to the door. 'Dandy and his wife will be around, anyway. You won't be alone with me.'

When he had gone Lissa stared at the closed door.

Somehow that promise of his was not so very reassuring, after all. Rape was not what she really feared—it was the insidious, tempting seduction of his hands and mouth which might prove really alarming. In spite of what she had said to him about not wanting him, she knew that all her own sensual instincts fought on his side whenever he touched her.

Her common sense and her intelligence warned her not to give in to him, but her senses clamoured for the pleasure he had begun to teach her. Lissa was not certain that in a straight fight between her mind and her body, her mind would win.

She had meant what she said about disliking his attitude. If she gave in to Luc's seductive caresses she would be exchanging the frying pan for the fire. Luc could destroy her every bit as much as Chris would have done. She had no intention of becoming his mistress for a few months until he tired of her. Her whole nature disposed her to feel sick at the very idea.

For most of her life she had been floating in a romantic mist, not seeing very clearly, not understanding herself or anyone around her. She had been fooled by Chris because of her naïve romantic blindness. Now she had grown up very rapidly and painfully and she was facing facts; not only about the world but about herself.

It had never occurred to her until recently that it was necessary to understand oneself. She had never known that she did not understand herself. The unthinking projection of her own personality which had gone on since she left the convent school had ended. The girl who had never noticed the sort of world she was living in had been a fool, and Lissa's own intelligence had sharpened at the realisation of it.

She had so much more to find out about herself, so much more to discover about the world, but of one thing she was absolutely certain; she was not the sort of girl who could blithely enter into a sexual relationship with a man she scarcely knew. She was strong enough to survive on her own—difficult though it might be—and she refused to trade her body for the sort of security Luc was presumably offering her.

The days when a woman had no choice but to do that were long gone. She was free and independent and she was her own mistress. She would not slide into becoming Luc's.

The following evening they drove to London through a windblown landscape whose bland, domestic contours seemed very strange to her eyes. Dusk was falling to shroud it as they drove, but she stared out at the countryside excitedly for as long as she could see it.

She kept comparing it with the fertile, vibrant colours and sounds of the island of her childhood. Everything she saw seemed to lack that drama—the empty great plains of Somerset, the neat little fields of Wiltshire, seemed colourless to her. But her fascination and surprise over the English countryside was as nothing compared to the traumatic cultural shock of London's overcrowded grey streets and bumper-to-bumper traffic.

Her head ached and throbbed, her eyes were dazed, her ears hummed with noise. Luc glanced at her and smiled faintly. 'Something of a shock, isn't it?'

It was quite dark now, but London seemed to blaze with light. Shops and street lights flared orange in the night. The city lay in a smoky flaring light which could be seen from a long way off—for a moment Lissa had almost thought it was on fire. They drove in over an enormous flyover and she stared down from the car, wincing at the spread of the city.

'I feel like Alice in Wonderland,' she said to Luc.

'You'll get used to it,' he promised her with a re-assuring glance. 'You can adapt to anything, believe me. In a few months you'll feel as if you've never lived anywhere else.'

Lissa wasn't sure she wanted to adapt to this crazy, surrealistic place. There were too many people, too much noise. Things rushed and pounded at her eyes and ears and she couldn't take any more of it in, her mind confused.

Luc obviously knew his way around the city. He turned into a stream of traffic going north and a few moments later they were purring down a quiet street of eighteenth-century houses. 'Regent's Park,' he informed her as he drew up outside one.

She looked at the house and although she knew nothing much about London she did not need great imagination to work out that this was the home of a wealthy man. Luc watched her wary, pale face.

Lissa was too tired to make any comment. When he got out and walked round to help her out of the car she let him steer her towards the house while Dandy took Luc's place at the wheel and drove the car away.

'Where's Dandy going?' she asked, halting.

'To park the car,' he said drily. 'The garage is round the corner.' He gave her a cool glance. 'He'll be back in a few moments.'

The door was suddenly flung open and a very short,

very thin woman rushed at Luc with her arms wide
and hugged him, kissing his cheek. 'You're later than
you said!'

'Traffic,' he said succinctly. When the thin arms released him he smiled down at the woman and said:
'This is Lissa, Megan.'

Lissa felt the quick searching stare of very bright
dark eyes. Megan was around fifty, she guessed, filled
with an energy which made her face vitally alive. Her
grey hair curled around that face. She wore a dark dress
which made her look thinner than ever and her voice
had a faint, soft lilt which Lissa could not identify.

'Hallo,' said Megan, holding out her hand.

Lissa shyly shook hands and Luc said: 'Megan is
Dandy's wife.'

Megan smiled at her. 'When he's home! One of these
days I'm going with them to find out what they get up
to on that boat.'

'You know you get as sick as a dog after five minutes,'
Luc told her, and she groaned.

'Isn't that the truth?' Her dark eyes smiled at Lissa.
'Are you a good sailor, Lissa?'

'Rotten,' said Luc, smiling. 'She was sick for most of
the voyage. We thought we might have to chuck her
overboard.'

Lissa flushed and Megan observed it with calm
amusement. 'Take no notice, love. Luc is a terrible
tease.'

The lilt had grown stronger and Lissa frowned, trying to work out what it was, but failing.

'That isn't an English accent, is it?'

'Welsh, love,' said Megan, with obvious satisfaction.

'She hasn't lived there for twenty years,' Luc drawled, 'but she clings to that accent like glue.'

'What's wrong with my accent?' Megan demanded.

'It's very beautiful,' said Lissa and Luc laughed.

'Tactful, isn't she?'

'People who don't like Welsh accents don't get any supper,' Megan assured him.

'I love them,' he said quickly, and got his ear pinched. 'Get inside, you!'

Luc waved Lissa into the house and followed her, talking to Megan cheerfully. Lissa looked around her with weary interest. They were standing in a cream-painted hall of spacious dimensions. Pale gilt medallions gleamed on the walls. A grandfather clock ticked in a deep, solemn voice near by. The carpet was deep and soft, a discreet shade of blue which was almost grey.

'Tired, love?' Megan asked her, making her jump.

She smiled and Luc said quietly: 'She's exhausted.'

'Bed for you, then,' said Megan. 'I'll take her up right away. She can have a tray in bed.'

Lissa followed her, barely aware of her surroundings now because her tiredness had become extreme. She stood in the bedroom to which Megan took her and shivered as though with a chill. Megan touched the radiator hidden behind a wood panelling. 'Cold, love?'

'Just tired,' Lissa admitted.

'Would you like me to help you get undressed?' Megan suggested.

Lissa shook her head. 'I'll be fine, thank you.'

'You slip into bed, then, and I'll be back with a tray,' said Megan, leaving her.

Lissa opened her case and took out one of her

nighties. Slowly she undressed, her body aching. When Megan returned Lissa was already asleep, her head buried on the pillow.

Megan turned off the bedside lamp and tiptoed out with the tray. Lissa half stirred as the light was doused, but sleep had her too deeply. She did not wake.

She did wake up, however, next morning, when she heard Megan drawing the curtains back. Megan turned with a smile. 'I brought you breakfast in bed,' Megan informed her. 'You look better this morning. You were dead to the world when I looked in last night.'

'I'm not used to travelling,' Lissa admitted.

'You'll have to get used to it with Luc,' Megan said with a little chuckle. 'He's born restless, always off to the other end of the world.'

She went out and Lissa buried her hot face in the pillow. Did Megan, too, expect her to become Luc's mistress? The thought made her so embarrassed and angry she wanted to scream.

She shouldn't have allowed him to bring her here. She was being put in a difficult position merely by being here in his house. Last night she had been too tired to think. Now she felt much more awake and aware, and as she looked around the pretty, expensively furnished room she felt her nerves prickle with anxiety.

Today she would go out and look for a job—any job that would take her away from Luc and the constant temptation of his inviting blue eyes and experienced hands.

She ate her breakfast while the morning light brightened the pale London sky. She heard birds calling somewhere outside and when she got up and went to the window she saw the trees of Regent's Park massed between two houses across the street. The elegant street was very quiet, but she could hear the far-off muted roar of London in the background. It reminded her of the sound of the sea which had been so constant a factor of life at St Lerie.

Later, dressed in a shirt and jeans, she went down the stairs with her tray. She paused in the hall, looking around her, and Luc appeared in a doorway, startling her.

'Oh!' she gasped. He looked very different today. He was wearing a formal dark striped suit, beneath which she could see a pale blue shirt and a rather sombre tie. That formality emphasised the razor edge of his profile, the cynical awareness of the blue eyes. Lissa looked at him and felt the enormous gulf between them, her heart wincing in pain.

'Megan says you slept well.' The deep cool drawl was very controlled. If she had first seen Luc looking like this, she realised, her impression of him would have been very different. He was not the mocking, reckless stranger she had known on St Lerie—this was a man sheathed in power and money, faintly remote, wearing authority like a gloss over his brown skin.

'I did. Thank you.' Her own voice was soft and polite, conscious of the distance between them.

'Put the tray on that table,' he said, glancing at it in her hand. 'Megan will collect it later.'

She put the tray down where he indicated and Luc waved her through the door of the room from which he had appeared. Lissa looked around it as she walked into it and was shaken by the unobtrusive elegance it presented. Luc came from a world she had never known before. She felt very out of place in her jeans and yellow shirt.

Closing the door, Luc stood watching her, one hand in his pocket, the other brushing back his black hair. 'What are your plans for today?' he enquired calmly.

She looked back at him. 'I must look for a job.'

Luc frowned slightly. 'There's no hurry.'

'There is for me.'

He ignored that. 'I have to go to the office this morning. Megan will take you on a shopping expedition.'

'Shopping? I haven't got enough money for ...'

'You won't make a very favourable impression on a prospective employer in jeans,' Luc interrupted drily.

'Oh,' she said, flushing. She had brought a mere handful of clothes with her and it had not occurred to her until now that this would be a problem.

'Don't worry about money,' Luc said casually. 'Megan will charge whatever you buy.'

'I can't take money from you!' Her skin was burning and her eyes were a vivid, angry green.

'You can pay me back,' he drawled, and she felt her back stiffen at something in his eyes as he said that.

She involuntarily took a backward step and Luc's cool manner became suddenly glacial. 'And I didn't mean what you thought I meant!'

Her eyes fell away from the angry stare of his and she muttered: 'I'm sorry.'

There was a silence, then he said almost wearily: 'Can't you trust me, Lissa? Is it too much to ask?'

She looked up. 'If I don't trust you, whose fault is that?'

His face hardened. 'We can't talk now,' he said

tersely. 'I have an appointment at eleven and I've got
to go. Promise me to stay with Megan until I get back.
She'll show you some of London. I don't want you
wandering off on your own.'

Lissa hesitated and Luc said forcibly: 'For God's
sake, does one day matter? Promise me!'

She nodded and he sighed faintly, turning to the
door. She felt reluctant to see him go suddenly. She
moved instinctively and he looked back at her over
his shoulder, the turn of the dark profile making her
heart turn over.

'You still haven't told me,' she said. 'What work do
you do?'

'I told you the truth,' Luc shrugged drily. 'I deal in
stocks and shares. I'm not a stockbroker, I'm a merchant
banker. For most of the year I'm so respectable it's
tedious. I break out of it to get away on the boat.'

'Banking?' she said in dazed disbelief. Whatever she
had expected to hear, it had not been that.

He laughed shortly. 'Your expression! Yes, I'm afraid
I'm what the newspapers call a "financier". I manage
other people's money.'

Lissa glanced slowly round the room. 'And you have
a lot of your own,' she muttered in grim realisation.

'I inherited it and I've increased it,' he admitted. 'I've
got quite a flair for investment—I told you, it's another form of gambling. There's always an element of
risk in it, but I was born with a sure instinct for the
market. You can't be taught how to predict market
fluctuation. You have to know by instinct and be ready
to take risks.'

'What if something happened when you were away

on the boat for weeks on end?' she asked, frowning. 'What if something went wrong in London?'

He laughed. 'There's a radio on the boat. I'm in constant touch with London. You don't think I leave anything to chance, do you? And I've got a brilliant team of men managing things while I'm away. I don't believe in keeping a dog and barking myself.' His blue eyes held a wry amusement. 'Far from being a risk it's the only thing that keeps me sane. I need to get away. I love sailing. Dandy and I have fought our way through a hundred storms—it's the sort of challenge I need.' He glanced at his watch again. 'I have to go, Lissa.'

'Yes,' she said huskily, and he glanced at her quickly, then he pulled open the door and went out without saying anything.

Lissa stood in the beautiful, gracious room staring around at the brocades and fine antique furniture. This was Luc's real background and she did not belong in it. The realisation made her stomach sink and her skin feel cold.

Luc had rescued her from Chris and maybe now he felt responsible for her, because he had brought her here into an environment for which she was not yet adjusted, but any help he gave her from now on would have strings attached to it. The more she let him involve himself in her life, the less hope she would have of ever getting away from him. The longer she stayed in his house the more likely it would become that she would end up as his mistress for as long as he wanted her. That prospect made Lissa shiver.

'There you are,' said Megan from the door, beaming at her. 'Luc says you want to see London. Where shall we go first?'

Lissa pulled herself together, imposing a bright smile. 'I've no idea. Where do you suggest?'

Megan eyed her jeans. 'Shopping first,' she said. 'It's best to do that while we're still full of energy.'

Looking around her later in Oxford Street Lissa could see that Luc was right about her clothes. She was going to need something other than jeans when she was interviewed by prospective employers. She would pay him back as soon as she had the money, she told herself. It disturbed her to accept money from him, but what choice did she have?

London stores fascinated her so much that she was reluctant to turn her attention to actually choosing anything at all. Megan tried to persuade her to buy a whole wardrobe of clothes, but Lissa obstinately settled for one discreet little dress in a smooth caramel shade. She bought shoes in a darker tone and a short camelhair jacket.

Disappointed, Megan kept urging her to look at other things. Lissa smiled at her. 'Please, I honestly don't want anything else,' she insisted, and Megan shrugged in defeat.

They began their tour of London after a quick lunch. Megan was a tireless guide. She showed Lissa every tourist attraction she could think of, pointing out famous landmarks on every side until Lissa's head ached and she couldn't take anything in at all.

They returned to the Regent's Park house in a taxi. Lissa was limp with exhaustion, but Megan seemed as lively as ever. Giving her a tolerant look, Megan told her to sit down while she made some tea. Lissa drifted wearily into the drawing-room and lay back in one of the deep, brocade-upholstered chairs, her eyes closed.

Her mind swam with impressions of a city whose every corner showed new surprises. The tropical luxuriance of St Lerie seemed already a vague and distant memory.

CHAPTER TEN

AFTER drinking the tea Megan brought her, Lissa went up to her room and took a long, leisurely bath in fragrant scented water, her tired body relaxing slowly as the heat invaded it.

She wore her new dress when she returned downstairs an hour later. Pausing at the drawing-room door, she heard the clink of glass. Luc was standing beside a table, pouring himself a glass of whisky from a decanter. He heard her movements and looked round, his glance sliding down over her with appraisal.

She flushed slightly, very aware of that cool inspection. She was waiting for some comment but Luc made none, turning back to the decanter. 'Would you like a drink, Lissa?'

'No, thank you.' She walked over to sit down on the chair in which she had been lying so wearily earlier that afternoon and a moment later Luc strolled over to sit down on the sofa, his long legs stretched out with a sigh. He was still wearing his formal city suit, but he had loosened his tie.

'I like the dress,' he said, staring at the whisky in his glass.

'Thank you.'

He sipped his whisky, still not looking at her, and Lissa sensed that he was absorbed in private thoughts, a faint line between his dark brows.

'It occurs to me that I could give you a job,' he said

suddenly, and Lissa looked at him, her eyes bitter with pain and anger.

'No, thank you! I'll find my own job.'

'There are openings at the bank,' he began, and Lissa sat up, shaking with the rage which was filling her.

'Do you think I'm completely stupid?'

Luc drained his whisky and stood up in a violent movement, his body tense. 'Yes,' he said through his teeth. 'I think you're deaf, dumb and blind and I'm tempted to give you a beating except that I doubt if even that would bring you to your senses.' He crashed his whisky glass down on the table and strode out, slamming the door.

She put her hands over her face, trembling. Luc's hard features had been stiff with hostility and a violence barely controlled. He had looked at her as if he hated her, and she found that so painful that she had to fight to stop the tears which were burning at the back of her eyes.

Luc was frustrated and his frustration had turned to rage. She found herself recoiling from that masculine fury, her whole body shaken by the revelation of it. It was wounding to have him look at her like that. She felt chilled and alone, bereft. Outside this lovely room lay a great, unknown city filled with millions of people she did not know. The only people she knew were in this house and of them the only one who mattered to her was Luc. The day she walked out of here she realised she would never see him again, and that thought made her stomach cramp in misery.

All her brave thoughts about independence seeped out of her. She shivered in the loneliness of a life without Luc, despising herself for the dread which thoughts of losing him inspired in her.

The evening softly darkened. The room lay quiet and still around her. She didn't move, crouched in the chair like a child, staring at emptiness with desolate eyes.

'Heavens, why didn't you put on the light?' Megan spoke briskly from the door and Lissa jumped at the sound of her voice. The room flowered with light, dazzling her eyes, and Megan gave a quick, searching look which took in the faint tear-stains and the pallor.

'Are you all right, love?'

'Just tired,' Lissa lied, smiling far too brightly.

'Are you sure?' Megan was frowning, concern in her dark eyes.

There was a movement behind her and Megan turned. Luc strolled past her saying coolly: 'Dinner ready?'

'In a moment,' said Megan. She was obviously on the point of saying something else, that frown still creasing her forehead, when Luc gave her one of the level, commanding looks which always made people jump to attention.

'I'm hungry.'

Megan made a brief face and vanished without another word. Luc had changed. Lissa flickered a nervous look over the dark velvet jacket, the cream evening shirt, before meeting his expressionless eyes.

'I'm sorry I lost my temper,' he told her evenly. 'I've had a difficult day.'

They dined alone, a fact of which Lissa was deeply aware, and the dining-room was lit by candles which threw strange shadows into the corners of the room and gave Luc's hard face a disturbing impact. Megan came in and out discreetly, saying nothing, her manner muted by the withdrawn expression on Luc's face. When once she lingered to say something to Lissa, Luc slowly turned his head and gave her a glance which sent her crossly out of the room, lips pursed.

Lissa had once found it hard to believe that Luc could do anything so mundane as work in the city, but having seen the authority and coolness of that face, she could believe it. His jaw had the assertive control of a man keeping a guard over his temper. He barely spoke and when he did his voice was clipped and unrevealing.

She couldn't even begin to guess what he was thinking. By the time they left the room she was grateful that the ordeal of that silent meal was over.

They took their coffee in the drawing-room. Megan brought in the tray and hovered, offering to pour it, but Luc shook his head. 'We'll do it ourselves.'

Megan went, shrugging. Lissa glanced at Luc through her lowered lashes. 'Shall I pour it?'

'Please,' he said curtly, taking up a position near the elegant fireplace, his arm lying along the mantel-shelf, his eyes fixed on the polished toe of his own shoe. She poured the coffee nervously and looked at him hesitantly. 'Do you want it there?'

He looked up as though startled to remember that she was present. 'No,' he murmured, coming over to take the cup from her. He sat down beside her on the sofa and she tensed. Luc did not speak, sipping his coffee with a bent head. Swallowing, Lissa asked: 'Have you lived here long?'

He put down his cup half finished and glanced at her.

'A good many years. Do you like the house?'

'It's very beautiful.' But overwhelming, she thought secretly. And rather empty. The whole house had a bland patina of grace which left one with the impression that it was a show place rather than a home.

Luc moved restlessly. 'Would you like a brandy with that?' He got up, went to the decanters and poured himself one, ignoring Lissa's polite little refusal. When he pressed a glass into her hand she looked up to protest and met those cool blue eyes, changing her mind. She anxiously tasted the brandy, shivering at the taste of it.

Luc drank his rapidly. The movement with which he put down the glass made her shoot him a wary look. He turned and took her barely touched glass, placing it beside his own.

'It's no good, Lissa,' he said tersely. 'I can't let you go.'

She stiffened and got up hurriedly. Luc was on his feet too at once, catching at her shoulder as she turned away. 'Where do you think you're going?'

'I'm not listening to any more ...' she began, and Luc's face became a mask of furious emotion.

'That's where you're wrong! You'll listen if I have to use force to make you.'

'Force is all you seem to understand,' she flung shakily. 'Just because you helped me get away from Chris you seem to think I belong to you.'

His face changed again, the blue eyes gleaming between those dark lashes, the dangerous anger vanishing. 'I'm glad you seem to be getting the idea at last,' he murmured silkily, and her colour rose in a hot wash.

'I don't belong to anyone but myself!'

'Don't you?' Luc's long fingers slid caressingly up her arm. He smiled at her tauntingly, amusement in his eyes. Lissa's heart was thudding in her throat and her mouth was dry. The hand at her shoulder gave a deft twist and to her horror she found herself pulled forward into Luc's arms before she could halt the movement.

Holding her, Luc sank back on to the sofa and she pushed at his wide shoulder as her face fell against him. He coolly lifted her chin with one hand and bent his head towards her. Fever ran through her veins like fire. The deep warmth of his mouth silenced all her protests. She sank into a languorous weakness, her arms stealing round his neck after a moment, giving herself up to the sensual delight he was making her feel.

When he lifted his head again she was still clinging, trembling from head to foot, her lips parted and aching from the long possession of his mouth.

Reluctantly, her eyes flicked open to meet the intent, brooding stare of his, and she felt her colour deepen further as she knew he was aware of the passion he had managed to arouse in her.

Harshly, he said, 'You're too young. I'm out of my mind, but I can't let you go.'

'I won't be your mistress!' Misery made her voice shake.

'Then will you be my wife?' he asked, his mouth twisting as though he found it hard to ask.

She stared disbelievingly, her eyes very wide.

'Don't look at me like that,' he muttered. 'I know I'm far too old for you. It's been driving me crazy ever since you told me how old you were. I told myself not to be a fool. I'm almost old enough to be your father.

But it was too late for me from the first minute we met on that beach.'

Her breathing shallow and irregular, her heart thudding, she whispered to him: 'Are you saying you love me?'

He sighed deeply, his eyes on her disbelieving face. 'That's what I'm saying.'

Lissa looked down, trying to take in what he had said. Staring at his hand as it lay against her waist, she asked in a low voice: 'If you really loved me why did you try to make me your mistress?'

Luc made a rough sound under his breath. 'I doubt if you'd understand if I told you. That's why I hesitated before I asked you to marry me. When you're thirty, Lissa, I'll be almost fifty. What sort of bargain am I for a girl of your age?'

She thought about that, her brows drawn, before looking up. 'You're saying that you thought it was one thing to have a brief affair with a girl of my age and another thing to actually marry her?'

His skin took on a dark red, the blue eyes hard. 'I suppose that's just what I did think. If I thought at all —and I wasn't doing much thinking whenever you were around. Lissa, try to understand—the minute I saw you I wanted you and as time went by I wanted you more and more. I was possessed by a driving necessity. However coolly I considered the actual facts, the minute I was with you all my calm intentions went out of the window and I was desperate to make love to you.'

She bit her lower lip, looking away from the urgent desire in his eyes. 'And when you consider the actual facts now, Luc, what do you really see? The same problem?'

He hesitated and she looked back at him levelly. Luc closed his eyes with a tormented twist of his mouth. 'Yes,' he muttered. 'You're too young and I'd be a swine if I married you. You ought to marry someone of your own age, someone suitable.' His voice had gone harsh and raw with an emotion she could feel in every fibre.

She watched him, feeling oddly aware and adult. Luc's cool strength had always outmatched her own, but the cynical sophistication which informed his hard features had dissolved now in a feeling which he could not hide.

'I'll start looking around for someone,' she said, and saw his lids open and the jealous, violent flash of the blue eyes.

'You damned well won't,' he bit out with his teeth snapping together. His arms tightened, hauling her closer, and he pushed his face into her ruffled hair. 'You'll marry me, Lissa, however insane it may be—because if you go away, I couldn't stand it.'

She didn't struggle, but she didn't respond. Lying in his arms, she said slowly: 'You still aren't thinking of me, though, are you, Luc? All you're thinking about is yourself, what you need.'

'If I think about what you need I'll have to let you go,' he said unevenly. 'It was for your sake that I hesitated to ask you to marry me. My God, are you so blind? Can't you see that it's you who'll suffer from having a husband so much older than yourself? I'm a gambler, Lissa, but even I hesitate at the odds against us. Do you think I don't realise that it's almost a certainty that one day you'll meet someone closer to your own age and want me to let you go?' He drew a long, fierce breath, the possessive grip hurting her as he held her even closer. 'And how could I refuse in the circumstances? It will kill me. But I'll have to agree.'

Lissa slid her arms round his neck, trembling, profoundly moved by the pain in his voice. 'No,' she whispered.

'I've been going round in circles for days thinking about it,' Luc said in a low voice. 'I was faced with an unenviable choice. Either I let you go now and went through hell or I married you and faced that hell some time in the future.'

'I love you,' she cried out in wild reaction to his anguished statement. 'Luc darling, I love you.' It was the first time she had allowed herself to admit it, and the stammered words made Luc tense, turning his face towards her in a blind movement which ended as their mouths met and clung hotly.

His hands gripped convulsively. He was so taut with a feverish desire that she felt his muscles clenching under her hands, his whole body coiled in barely restrained hunger.

Lissa moaned, her eyes clouding with answering passion, and Luc's mouth bruised and demanded, the heavy pace of his heart matching the wild tattoo of her own.

'I want you so badly, Liss,' he breathed into her mouth. Lifting his head he looked almost dazedly at her, his face set in that mask of unveiled desire. 'I've never felt like this in my life before. The morning we met on that beach you knocked me right off my feet and I've never managed to get back up again since. Every time I look at you I burn to touch you.'

Her mouth was dry. 'Take me to bed,' she whispered through her trembling lips. 'Now, Luc.'

She saw the feverish flare of his blue eyes and for a second she thought he was going to pick her up and carry her upstairs. Then he swallowed, the muscles of the strong throat moving painfully. He shook his head, his mouth wry.

'A week ago I'd have been up the stairs so fast I'd have fallen on my face,' he said grimly. 'I meant to seduce you, Liss. I knew I could if I tried.'

Her face flushed even more deeply, her eyes half angry, and he grimaced.

'I'm sorry for how that sounds, but your responses made it obvious right from the start. I saw you with Brandon and I knew he wasn't doing a thing to you, but when I started kissing you, I felt the response coming at me in waves. You're very inexperienced, darling, but I'm not.'

She winced and he gave her a faint sighing smile. 'I wish I was, believe me. I wish I could match you on that level, but I can't. I've had affairs before. What else could you expect? At my age I thought affairs were all I was ever going to have. I'd never met a woman who made me feel I could bear to live with her for life. And when I did meet her I had to fall headlong for a girl of twenty!'

Lissa watched him, anxiety in her eyes. The age gap between them had never bothered her as much as it obviously bothered him. The only gulf she had felt was the gulf of experience which gave him such an advantage over her.

'When I managed to get you away from Brandon, I

intended to seduce you into an affair,' Luc admitted flatly. 'I refused to look too far into the future at that stage because I was already sick at the thought that one day you'd be tired of me, but I had to have you, Lissa. I was ready to take whatever I could get you to give me.'

'How can you think I would tire of you?' she asked huskily, touching his face with one hand, gently following the line of cheek and jaw.

She felt his bones tighten under her fingers. 'You don't know what you're saying,' Luc muttered.

'I know that I refused to have an affair with you because I knew it would kill me if you got tired of me,' she whispered.

He turned his head to kiss her palm, his eyes closing. 'Never. Never in this life, darling.'

'You said you wanted me to trust you,' Lissa murmured. 'Can't you trust me? Can't you believe I love you and will go on loving you for ever?'

His mouth twisted in that movement of pain. 'I've got to—I can't face the alternative. My father used to say that when you can't face looking too far ahead, the only way to live is from day to day, putting one foot in front of another without thinking about tomorrow. That's what I'm going to have to do, Lissa. I'm going to live each day as it comes along, and forget about the future. If I'm going to lose you one day, I prefer not to think about it.'

'You won't lose me,' she promised.

'If you ever do want to go,' he began, and she put her fingers over his mouth.

'I never shall.'

He kissed the fingers, then lifted them away to ask huskily: 'When will you marry me?'

'When do you want me?' she asked, teasing him gently with a little smile.

'My God—now,' he groaned, then said thickly, 'But I'm going to wait because when I do take you I want to be sure you're mine. I've got a superstitious streak— most gamblers have. If I don't marry you before I take you to bed, I'm afraid I'll lose you even sooner. We'll start life together properly or not at all.'

'Will your family object to you marrying someone without a family or money?' she asked, frowning.

'My family depend on me, not the other way around,' he said drily. 'I shan't be asking their permission or even their approval. Don't worry. There aren't many of them, and they'll smile from ear to ear, because if any one of them offended you I'd make him regret it to his dying day.'

She surveyed him, noting the change in his face and the hard note in his voice. 'You're ruthless, aren't you?'

He grinned briefly. 'Lissa, I control the money in the family. Believe me, they'll welcome you with open arms.'

'And cynical,' she added thoughtfully.

He laughed. 'The tougher they are, the harder they fall,' he mocked lightly, but the blue eyes were brilliant with passion as he watched her.

'Even if I'd seduced you on the boat I suspect I'd have ended up on my knees begging you to marry me,' he said drily. 'When it came to the point I'd have done anything in my power to keep you.'

'All you have to do to keep me, is love me,' Lissa told him.

'My God, Lissa, I can't begin to tell you how much I love you,' he groaned.

'You can try,' she said softly.

'Oh, I intend to,' said Luc as he bent his head to kiss her again.

Harlequin Presents...

The books that let you escape
into the wonderful world of romance!
Trips to exotic places... interesting
plots... meeting memorable people...
the excitement of love....These are
integral parts of Harlequin Presents—
the heartwarming novels read by
women everywhere.

Many early issues are now available.
Choose from this great selection!

Choose from this great selection of exciting Harlequin Presents editions

Relive a great romance...
with Harlequin Presents

Complete and mail this coupon today!

Harlequin Reader Service

In U.S.A.
MPO Box 707
Niagara Falls, N.Y. 14302

In Canada
649 Ontario St.
Stratford, Ontario, N5A 6W2

Please send me the following Harlequin Presents novels. I am enclosing my check or money order for $1.50 for each novel ordered, plus 59¢ to cover postage and handling.

☐ 192	☐ 201	☐ 210
☐ 193	☐ 202	☐ 211
☐ 194	☐ 203	☐ 212
☐ 195	☐ 204	☐ 213
☐ 197	☐ 205	☐ 214
☐ 198	☐ 206	☐ 215
☐ 199	☐ 207	☐ 216
☐ 200	☐ 208	☐ 217

Number of novels checked @ $1.50 each = $_____

N.Y. and Ariz. residents add appropriate sales tax. $_____

Postage and handling $_____.59

TOTAL $_____

I enclose _____
(Please send check or money order. We cannot be responsible for cash sent through the mail.)

Prices subject to change without notice.

NAME _____
(Please Print)

ADDRESS _____

CITY _____

STATE/PROV. _____

ZIP/POSTAL CODE _____

Offer expires October 31, 1981

10256317